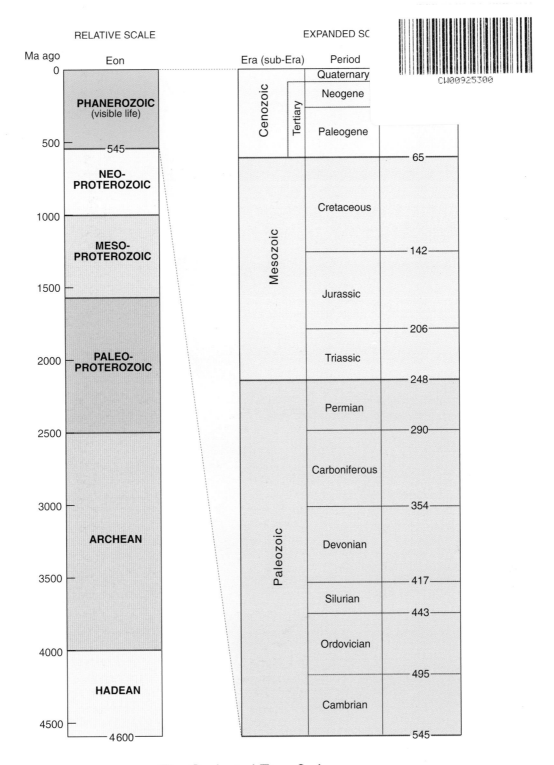

The Geological Time-Scale

Science: Level 3

S339 Understanding the continents

Block 1 Earth's Engine

Prepared for the Course Team by Hazel Rymer and Steve Drury

The S339 Course Team

Chair

Nigel Harris

Course Manager

Jessica Bartlett

Other members of the Course Team

Mandy Anton *(Designer)*

Tom Argles *(Author)*

Gerry Bearman *(Editor)*

Steve Blake *(Block 3 Chair, Author)*

Steve Drury *(Block 5 Chair, Author)*

Professor Wes Gibbons, University of Wales, Cardiff *(Course Assessor)*

Nigel Harris *(Block 4 Chair, Author)*

Lee Johnson *(Graphic Artist)*

Martin Kemp *(BBC Producer)*

Dave McGarvie *(Author)*

Jann Matela *(Word Processing)*

Ray Munns *(Cartographer)*

Pam Owen *(Graphic Artist)*

Ian Parkinson *(Reader/Author)*

Professor Julian Pearce, University of Wales, Cardiff *(Course Assessor)*

Nick Rogers *(Block 2 Chair, Author)*

Hazel Rymer *(Block 1 Chair, Author)*

Val Russell *(original Course Manager)*

Andy Sutton *(Software Designer)*

Peter Twomey *(Editor)*

John Whalley, University of Portsmouth *(Consultant Author)*

The Course Team gratefully acknowledges the contributions of those who produced the first editions of this Course, from which parts of this Block have been derived. In addition, we would like to thank the students, Associate Lecturers and assessors from other institutions who commented on drafts of this new edition. Other contributors to S339 are acknowledged in specific credits.

This publication forms part of an Open University course S339 *Understanding the continents*. The complete list of texts which make up this course can be found at the back. Details of this and other Open University courses can be obtained from the Student Registration and Enquiry Service, The Open University, PO Box 197, Milton Keynes MK7 6BJ, United Kingdom: tel. +44 (0)845 300 60 90, email general-enquiries@open.ac.uk

Alternatively, you may visit the Open University website at http://www.open.ac.uk where you can learn more about the wide range of courses and packs offered at all levels by The Open University.

To purchase a selection of Open University course materials visit http://www.ouw.co.uk, or contact Open University Worldwide, Walton Hall, Milton Keynes MK7 6AA, United Kingdom for a brochure. tel. +44 (0)1908 858793; fax +44 (0)1908 858787; email ouw-customer-services@open.ac.uk

The Open University, Walton Hall, Milton Keynes, MK7 6AA

First published 2003. Reprinted 2009.

Edited and designed by The Open University.

Typeset by The Open University.

Printed in the United Kingdom by Cambrian Printers, Aberystwyth

ISBN 978 1 8487 3205 6

4.1

Contents

Earth's engine: introduction

The surface of the Earth is made up of oceans and continents. Although the oceans cover the greater area, it is upon the continents that human evolution has taken place, and from the continents that evidence for the long-term complexities of Earth history has been recovered. It is perhaps true to say that by studying oceanic lithosphere we understand how the Earth works today, but the continents provide most of the evidence for how the planet has evolved through time. This Course will develop your understanding of the continents.

The central theme of the first Block in this Course is plate tectonics. Integrating the text with Activities (which include DVDs), you will build on your previous studies. In Section 1, the evidence for plate tectonics is presented and the forces acting on plates and the various types of interactions between plates are reviewed. Recent results from seismic tomography are introduced, and provide evidence for how the mantle moves beneath the lithospheric plates.

Plate tectonics is the surface manifestation of thermal processes at depth, and, in Section 2, the generation and transfer of heat within the Earth is described. The response of the lithosphere to thermal and mechanical stress is discussed in Section 3. Armed with this information, you will be ready to study Section 4 which looks in detail at the plate boundaries of north-east Japan and Costa Rica in the light of the thermal and mechanical constraints on plate tectonics.

Block 1 provides a platform from which the nature of rifting and continental break-up (Block 2), continental evolution at subduction zones (Block 3) and continental collision (Block 4) will be addressed. By the end of the Course (Block 5), you will be ready to re-examine the geological heritage of Britain using world examples of continental geology.

Now it is time to start to understand the continents.

1   Continental drift and plate tectonics

The plate-tectonic theory for the evolution of the oceanic lithosphere and continental drift hinges on several discoveries. Francis Bacon (a philosopher in the reign of Elizabeth I) had the earliest idea that the continents either side of the Atlantic Ocean may once have been united. Soon after the first passable maps of the Atlantic began to take shape in the late 16th century, Bacon pondered on the apparent jigsaw-like fit of the Atlantic continental margins. The idea that the present-day continents fit closely together was supported by compelling geological evidence presented first by Alfred Wegener in 1912 and later through modelling using spherical geometry by Edward Bullard and colleagues in 1965.

Figure 1.1 summarizes geological information which you may have met in your previous studies.

⬤   What are the main lines of geological evidence that the continents have drifted, other than the matching shape of continental margins?

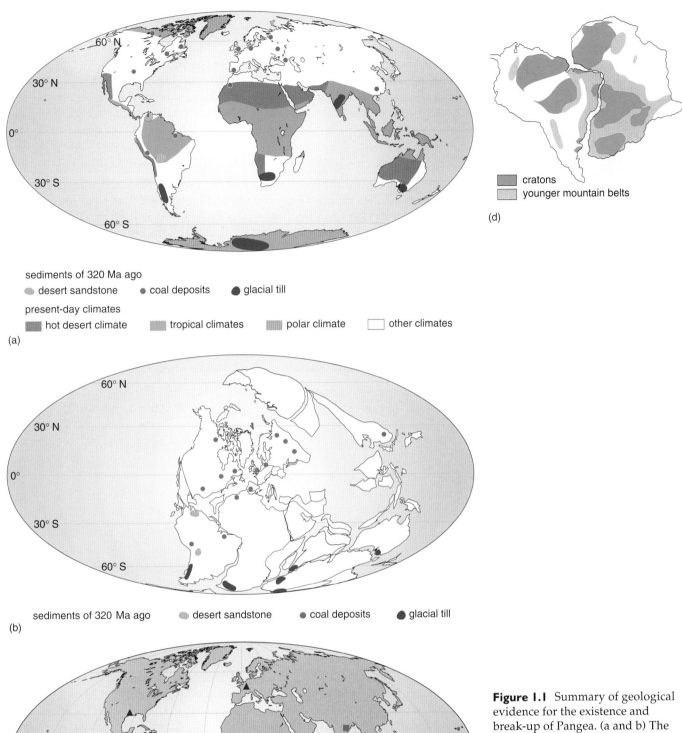

sediments of 320 Ma ago

⬭ desert sandstone   ● coal deposits   ⬤ glacial till

present-day climates

▨ hot desert climate   ▨ tropical climates   ▨ polar climate   ☐ other climates

(a)

sediments of 320 Ma ago   ⬭ desert sandstone   ● coal deposits   ⬤ glacial till

(b)

▨ cratons
▨ younger mountain belts

(d)

● *Mesosaurus*   ▲ *Edaphosaurus*   ■ *Glossopteris*

(c)

Figure 1.1 Summary of geological evidence for the existence and break-up of Pangea. (a and b) The difference between present-day climatic conditions and those found on the continents 320 Ma ago suggests that the continents have moved. (c) The occurrence of identical fossils either side of large oceans suggests that continental drift has occurred. (d) Both Archean (older than 2000 Ma) and late Precambrian (600–2000 Ma) rock outcrops match exactly in South America and Africa.

⬤ The most important evidence is the occurrence of Carboniferous to Permian glacial strata on all the southern continents. These tillites, and the glacially grooved 'pavements' on which they rest, now span latitudes from 70° S (Antarctica) to 20° N (India). Assembling this evidence for glaciation at sensibly high southern latitudes involves packing the southern continents together. Only a limited range of assemblies is consistent with a radial arrangement of the grooves cut by a flowing ice sheet, centred roughly on the area of maximum ice accumulation, presumably close to the South Pole at the time. This reassembly also places the Carboniferous coalfields and deserts at the latitudes where they would form in modern climatic conditions. This universal clumping, in what Wegener called Pangea (from the Greek for 'all Earth'), also helped resolve the mystery of almost identical plants and land vertebrates in the Permian fossil records of the southern continents and those of eastern North America and western Europe. The third main plank supporting Wegener's notion of Pangea is that the refit neatly juxtaposes orogenic belts older than the Carboniferous across the joins.

1.1   Magnetic evidence

The supercontinent of Pangea broke up into segments and began to drift. Charting the drift of these segments through time became possible with the development of means for measuring the direction and inclination of the ancient magnetic field. The Earth's magnetic field can be modelled to a first approximation as a dipolar field. If the Earth's rotational axis more or less coincides with the axis of its dipolar magnetic field, then the inclination of the field will range from vertical at the poles to horizontal at the mid-point between them — approximately around the Equator (Figure 1.2). Indeed, measuring magnetic inclination from the dip of a compass needle is a crude means of estimating latitude. When the magnetic and rotational axes do not coincide, true and magnetic north will differ. This offset, called declination, is currently about 2° in London, and has varied by more than 30° since observation began more than 400 years ago.

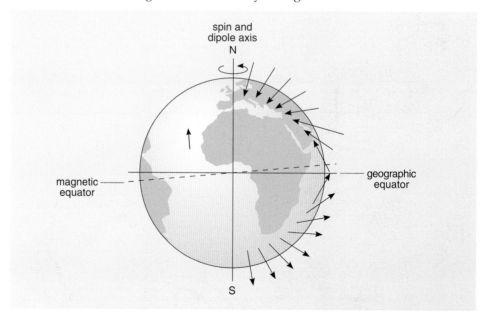

Figure 1.2   Inclination is the angle at which a compass needle rests relative to horizontal (arrows on the right-hand side). Declination is the angle that a compass points away from geographic north (5° west for the arrow on the left).

Naturally magnetic materials, such as the iron oxide mineral magnetite (Fe_3O_4), develop a magnetization induced temporarily by the Earth's present magnetic field (**induced magnetism**), but they also retain permanent magnetism which dates from the time that the material formed. Such **remanent magnetism** may involve magnetic minerals crystallizing from magma. When the magma temperature falls below a critical point, grains of such minerals become magnetic dipoles, aligned parallel to the Earth's prevailing field. Their inclination (dip of the magnetic field) depends on the latitude at which crystallization took place. Permanent magnetism also occurs in sedimentary rocks. Magnetic grains align themselves parallel to the Earth's magnetic field as crystals grow, as grains settle in water, or even simply through long exposure to a particular magnetic field. So, rocks themselves are weakly magnetic, depending on their content of minerals like magnetite.

Distinguishing the natural remanent magnetism, locked into a rock when it formed, from its present induced magnetism, is the principle behind estimating the **paleolatitude** of continental segments. That depends on the *inclination* of the remanent magnetism, after correction for any tilting by folding or faulting. The *direction* of remanent magnetism reveals how crustal segments have rotated during continental drift. For any continental segment, it is therefore possible to chart the variation through time of both its latitude and its rotation assuming that the pole remains fixed. Alternatively, assuming the segment actually remains fixed, the 'apparent' movement of the pole can be calculated, producing an apparent polar wander curve. Two measurements of remanent magnetism from rocks of approximately the same age from the same segment define either one of these two things. These two ways of interpreting magnetic evidence are illustrated in Figure 1.3a and b.

⬤ What is the remaining unknown in such a geographical reconstruction?

⬤ There is no means of determining the associated longitude with absolute certainty. That is a matter to which we return shortly.

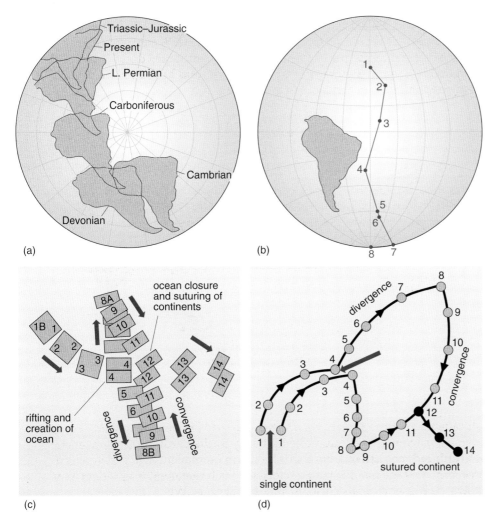

(a)

(b)

(c)

(d)

Figure 1.3 (a) The drift of South America from Cambrian through to present times (*note:* this centres on the South Pole). (b) The same paleomagnetic information in (a) expressed as the apparent polar wandering curve for South America, with North Pole at top. (c) Cartoon showing a plate-tectonic history that involves drift of a single continental segment (1–4), its rifting into two parts and their independent motion (5–11), until at time 12 they collide to reunite once more, but not along the original line of rifting. Steps 12–14 show the path taken by the reassembled continent. (d) The history in (c) expressed as apparent polar wandering paths for the two parts that comprised the continent from time 12–14. The two paths do not coincide for the time before rifting (4), because they did not reunite at time 12 along the same line as they rifted apart at time 4. The 'hairpin' bends at time 8 signify that the ocean separating the two fragments ceased to get wider and began to close.

It is unlikely that the magnetic poles have migrated far from the geographical poles as their position is influenced by the Earth's spin axis which has remained constant at least since the continents have existed. That is why such curves are said to be 'apparent'. However, plotting the shift with time of all continental segments produces a confusing jumble on diagrams like Figure 1.3a. Comparing apparent polar wander curves for several continents is easier to deal with, and Figure 1.3c and d compares the two options in cartoon form.

Measuring the intensity (strength) of the magnetic field over the oceans stemmed from development of submarine detection systems during the Second World War. Oceanographic geophysicists subtracted the average present-day magnetic field (most easily measured from high-altitude aircraft) from that measured much more precisely by magnetometers towed behind low-flying aircraft or ships. The difference between the two reveals magnetic-field anomalies. What emerged from a few traverses across oceanic areas were regular variations in the total-field intensity. Some were higher than average (positive anomalies) and some were lower (negative). The intriguing regularity in the data led to large-scale systematic ocean-magnetic surveys. They not only confirmed the regular cycles of positive and negative anomalies, but showed that they were in the form of stripes roughly parallel to the trends of oceanic ridge systems. The key discovery was that the shapes of the anomalous stripes (their detailed variation in wavelength and amplitude) were approximately symmetrical across the ridges — the anomaly patterns on one side of a ridge mirrored those on the other.

● What were the two main conclusions from the sea-floor magnetic anomaly patterns?

● (i) The positive and negative anomaly patterns might represent repeated reversals in the polarity of the Earth's magnetic field. (ii) The symmetry of patterns across oceanic ridge systems suggested a systematic change in the age of the anomalies away from the ridges, so that the oceanic crust from which the anomalies must derive was laterally zoned in age.

Correlation of ocean-floor magnetic anomalies with detailed timings of magnetic reversals obtained from continental lavas suggested that the ocean crust became progressively older away from the ridges. The stripes showed that the ocean floors were spreading away from the ridges (Figure 1.4). Dating of the oldest sediments lying on oceanic crust confirmed the **sea-floor spreading** hypothesis.

The names given to the various recent magnetic epochs are shown. Magma generation at ocean ridges laterally displaces older oceanic crust and, together with the magnetic features that it produces, provides:

1 a mechanism for continental drift;

2 a means of charting the evolution of ocean floor since 170 Ma by progressively removing older and older strips of ocean floor from the ridge axes;

3 a means of detecting different spreading rates, from the varying widths of the stripes for different age ranges, both in different oceans and during the evolution of individual oceans;

4 a means of detecting changes in the direction of sea-floor spreading, and the position of now-extinct ridges, from changes in the orientation of magnetic stripes.

Continental drift and sea-floor spreading lie at the heart of the theory of **plate tectonics**. Patterns of magnetic stripes over the ocean basins divide them into a mosaic of blocks, each of which forms a coherent whole (see the wallchart *This Dynamic Planet*, DP). Boundaries between the blocks have distinct kinds of earthquake activity (Section 1.2) that imply three main types of interaction

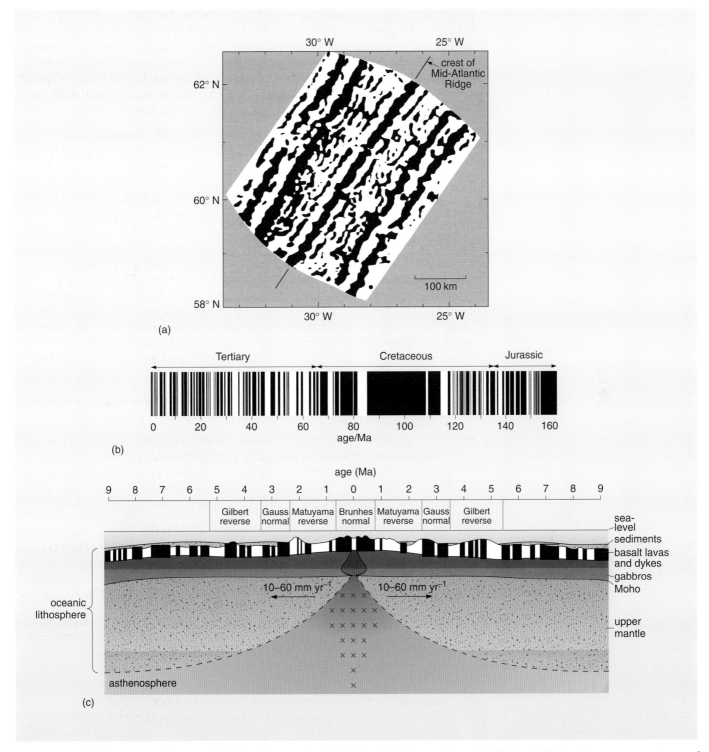

Figure 1.4 (a) Symmetry of magnetic 'stripes' across the Mid-Atlantic Ridge south-west of Iceland. Dark stripes represent normal (present day) polarity. (b) Recent (Tertiary) to Jurassic magnetic polarity record showing multiple changes in polarity. Most magnetic epochs last a million years or so, but a period of normal magnetization in the middle of the Cretaceous lasted over 20 million years. (c) Schematic cross-section of an oceanic ridge system, showing the sequence of polarity changes in the last 9 Ma.

between blocks. The rarity of earthquakes within the blocks suggests that they do not respond to the stresses involved in their motion: they behave as rigid plates. Some of the plates include continents, and carry those continents as passive components. Plates comprise the lithosphere, oceanic and continental, and their definition depends on both thermal and mechanical properties to which we shall return in Sections 2 and 3.

1.2   Plate motions and interactions

Oceanic and continental lithosphere make up the plates. The amount of each type of lithosphere varies from plate to plate and also varies through time. The Pacific Plate is dominantly oceanic, but the South American Plate is made up of both oceanic and continental lithosphere.

● Can you remember the three types of plate boundary?

● They are constructive, destructive and conservative.

The Earth's main plates are shown in Figure 1.5 together with the three kinds of plate boundary and the rates at which new oceanic lithosphere forms at constructive margins — the sea-floor spreading rates. The half-rates either side of a constructive margin, the directions of spreading and the convergence rates at subduction zones show the motions of plates relative to one another. Plates do not stay the same size. For example, the proportion of oceanic lithosphere in the South American Plate is increasing due to sea-floor spreading in the South Atlantic. We shall look at the evolution of lithosphere and the nature of the part of the Caribbean Plate occupied by Central America in the associated video as part of Activity 4.1 at the end of Section 4.

The generation of new oceanic lithosphere at ridges increases the surface area of the ocean floors. However, unless the Earth's radius also increases, the continental surface and old oceanic surface must reduce at the same rate. Recycling back to the mantle of older oceanic lithosphere therefore balances the addition of new material. Magnetic data provided the evidence for sea-floor spreading in Wegener's theory of continental drift, which he had been unable to resolve to the satisfaction of most geologists. Resolving the 'space problem' that sea-floor spreading presented required evidence from seismicity and bathymetric features of the ocean basins.

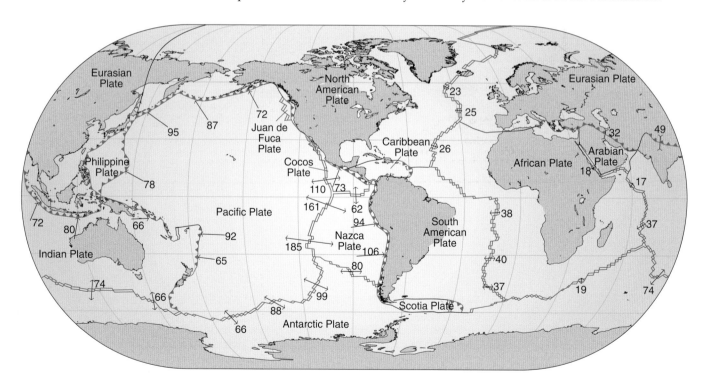

KEY   // divergent (constructive) plate boundary   ⌐ convergent (destructive) plate boundary   / transform fault (conservative) plate boundary

Figure 1.5   Lithospheric plates and boundaries. Red lines (e.g. along the middle of the Atlantic) indicate constructive plate boundaries. Blue lines and black lines indicate destructive and conservative boundaries respectively. Thin black arrows at constructive boundaries show the direction and rates of spreading, arrow length being proportional to speed. The associated numbers are for full spreading rates in mm yr⁻¹. Arrows at destructive margins are proportional to relative plate movement there.

Plate boundaries are defined by earthquake zones of two kinds: (i) those with shallow foci, along all the oceanic ridges (e.g. mid-Atlantic) that display symmetrical magnetic patterns, active zones of continental rifting (e.g. East Africa) and zones of continent–continent collision (e.g. Alps–Caucasus–Himalaya chain) that previously involved subduction; and (ii) those with foci descending as deep as 600 km associated with oceanic trench systems, volcanic island arcs (e.g. Japan), and continental margins that have volcanoes (e.g. the Andes). Details of the distribution of earthquakes appear on the wall chart *This Dynamic Planet* (DP), together with continental and sea-floor topography, and the distribution of active volcanoes.

Bathymetric features trending perpendicular to ridge axes displace the magnetic stripes and the ridge axes, suggesting that they are vertical faults of some kind. However, only shallow seismicity occurs between the ridge offsets. These fracture zones are termed **transform faults**.

> **Question 1.1** Draw a simple sketch of a transform fault showing the sense in which it displaces a ridge and magnetic stripes, and the fault's sense of active motion. Make notes describing your diagram.

The oceanic parts of several plates show chains of islands, and increasingly precise bathymetry reveals that these chains continue much further as lines of seamounts below sea-level on the ocean floor (see DP). The Hawaiian chain of the North Pacific Ocean is the best example (Figure 1.6a). It links with the

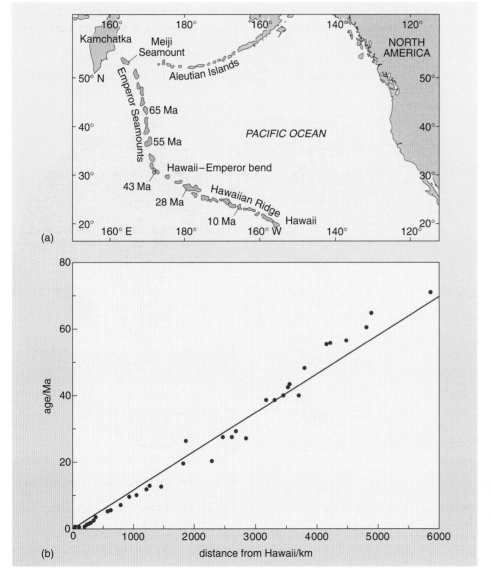

(a)

(b)

Figure 1.6 (a) The Hawaii–Emperor chain of the northern Pacific. (b) Plot of age versus distance from the volcanically active part of the chain, with a best-fit line through sample points.

Emperor Seamount chain, but goes in a different direction. The main Hawaiian Islands are volcanic in origin, but they lie far from any mid-ocean ridge system or subduction zone. The smaller islands to the WNW are extinct basaltic volcanoes, and samples dredged from the seamount chains are volcanic in origin too. Accurate radiometric ages have now been obtained for samples from the entire length of the Hawaii–Emperor chain. They show a remarkably regular increase in age along the chain, away from volcanically active Hawaii (Figure 1.6b), going back to the earliest Tertiary (about 60 Ma).

> **Question 1.2** (a) Using information from Figure 1.6 and by looking at the relevant part of DP, state how the ages along the Hawaii–Emperor chain relate to the ages of adjacent ocean floor. (b) Calculate the average speed at which the chain has grown since 40 Ma from a best-fit line to the data. (c) How does this speed compare with that for those parts of the chain older than 40 Ma? Can you suggest a reason for any change?

The significance of the information for oceanic island and seamount chains, like those linked to Hawaii, is that they must have formed within pre-existing oceanic lithosphere which has moved over the source of magma. The magma source is a hot spot and currently active hot spots have active volcanoes above them. A chain of extinct volcanoes (getting older with increasing distance) runs away from the present position of the hot spot. For any individual chain, it is impossible to say confidently that its source hot spot has remained fixed in the mantle beneath the asthenosphere; it too may have moved, but at a different rate from the lithosphere above it. However, if you look at the other chains in the Pacific on DP, you will see that they are all roughly parallel to either the Hawaii chain or the Emperor chain, and that the age–length relations are roughly similar. This is strong evidence that all of their source hot spots have remained fixed for at least the last 70 Ma. This observation is the basis for the **hot spot frame of reference** for calculating the **absolute** or **true motions** of existing plates over the last 70 to 80 Ma. The bend in the Hawaii–Emperor chain shows that a profound shift in absolute motion of the Pacific Plate occurred about 40 Ma ago. Since then, the Pacific Plate has moved WNW at about 85 mm yr^{-1}.

- How does this compare with the rate and direction of spreading from the East Pacific Rise?

- It is more or less the same.

In that regard, the Pacific Plate is unique. Information from other hot-spot related chains, on the ocean floor and in a few cases on continents, shows considerable variation in the past patterns of relative plate motions (Figure 1.5 and DP). Information on plate speed and direction can be used to infer previous locations of plates, but also their future locations. It is speculative to look very far into the future, but at the present rates of movement the plates will have shifted a long way from their current positions in 50 Ma time. Absolute plate motions are shown in Figure 1.7 as arrows proportional to the distance that points on each plate would travel during the next 50 Ma, if the motions stay as they have been for the last 40 Ma or so.

The three main features associated with plate tectonics are the different kinds of plate boundary: **constructive** (i.e. seismically active oceanic ridges), **destructive** (i.e. subduction zones, also known as Wadati–Benioff zones), and **conservative** boundaries (i.e. transform faults). The forces acting on the tectonic plates and the nature of the plate boundaries are subjects for the rest of Section 1. The

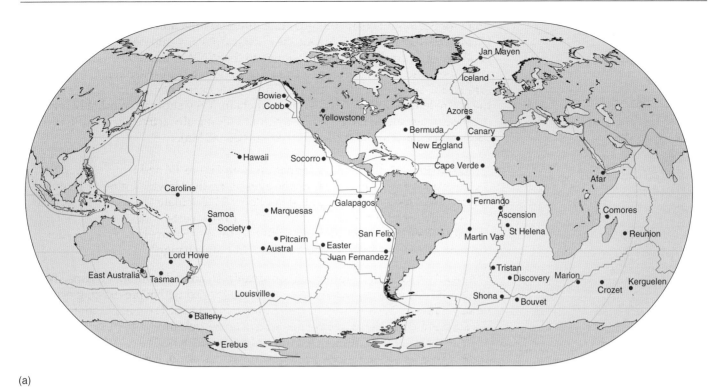

(a)

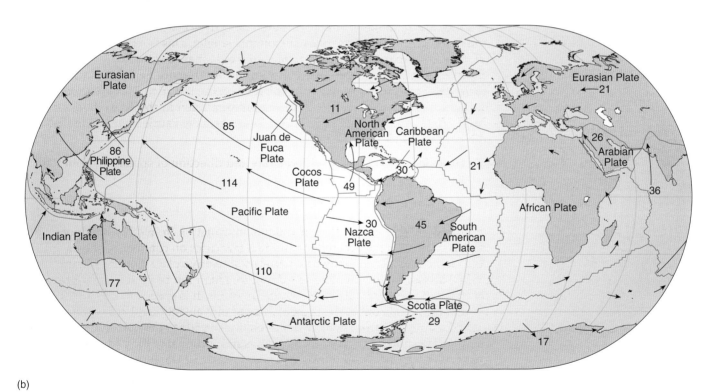

(b)

Figure 1.7 Motion of lithospheric plates relative to hot spots (red dots in (a)) shown as arrows (in (b)) with arrow length proportional to the distance that points on the plates would travel during the next 50 Ma. In a hot spot frame of reference, the motions shown are absolute. The numbers are the current mean true plate speed in mm y^{-1}.

processes driving plate tectonics and defining the nature of the lithospheric response are reviewed in Sections 2 and 3. The volcanic rocks associated with hot spots and the processes that generate them form important topics in Block 2.

Activity 1.1

Now attempt Activity 1.1 on the course website. There, you will use DP, together with other resources, to investigate different aspects of the tectonics of the Pacific and Indo-Australian Plates. You should take about 45 minutes to do this Activity.

Activity 1.2

You should now attempt Activity 1.2. This is a computer-based activity and involves viewing a PowerPoint presentation animating the last 50 Ma of evolution of the western Pacific. You should take about 30 minutes to do this Activity.

1.3   Forces acting on plates

The present-day lithospheric plates were formed by the splitting up of previous plate assemblies resulting in part from plate movement over hot spots. Plates can be several tens of km thick and thousands of square km in area, so enormous forces are required to move them. The largest forces act at the edges of the plates, but all the most important forces are shown on Figure 1.8. Conventionally, forces that oppose motion are termed R (for resistive) and forces that encourage movement are termed F (for forcing); subscript letters indicate the origin of the force. The presence of earthquakes is evidence for resistance to movement and at constructive plate margins, shallow earthquakes (see DP) and transform faults are manifestations of **ridge resistance** (R_R) and **transform resistance** (R_{TF}). The overall topography of ocean basins contributes to forces that encourage sea-floor spreading, because the sea-floor becomes deeper away from ridges. As the lithosphere ages, it cools to become more dense and less buoyant than newly formed lithosphere at ridge axes. Gravity acts to pull the lithosphere down this gentle slope away from ridges, giving a **ridge–slide force** (F_{RS}). Viscous drag in the mantle at the base of the oceanic lithosphere opposes that motion giving **oceanic drag resistance** (R_{OD}).

At destructive margins, old, cold and dense oceanic lithosphere descends into the mantle, becoming denser still when its basaltic cap transforms to eclogite (garnet–pyroxene rock with the composition of basalt) by metamorphic change. Gravity imparts a **negative buoyancy force** (F_{NB}) that acts vertically downwards. The effect of this force further up the subducting slab is to pull the plate towards the subduction zone and imparts the **slab–pull force** (F_{SP}). Resisting this movement is the drag on the top and bottom surfaces of the descending slab (**slab resistance** R_S) and the work done in bending the slab downwards (**bending resistance** R_B). The overriding plate resists the movement on the downgoing plate at the plate

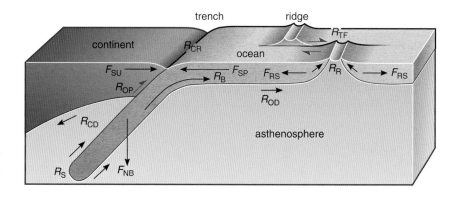

Figure 1.8   The most important forces connected with plate tectonics, divided into those actively encouraging movement (F) and those resisting it (R). Subscripts are defined in the text.

margin producing **overriding plate resistance** (R_{OP}), and beneath the continental plate, resistance to the necessary mantle movement is manifest as **continental drag** (R_{CD}). The need for the overriding plate to bend towards the trench associated with subduction, creates a slope. Gravitational forces therefore act on the overriding plate as if to 'suck' it into the trench and give **trench suction force** (F_{SU}). Destructive margins involve both plates in collision to give a **colliding resistance** (R_{CR}) that acts in opposite directions on both plates.

Some forces are stronger than others and an added complication is that forces do not remain constant in magnitude or direction through time. However, since plates obviously do move, we can draw a simple conclusion: the global sum of all the forces encouraging movement is greater than the resistive force, and the continuous magnetic record of today's oceans shows without doubt that it has been so, at least back to the Jurassic Period.

● Of all the forces, which is the largest?

● Slab–pull force, with ridge–slide force coming second. The other forces have only local significance.

This answer has an important implication. The difference between the world's two largest spreading oceans is that the Pacific Plate is being actively subducted (see DP) and the Atlantic Plate is not. Atlantic spreading rates are about a quarter those of the Pacific, almost certainly because of the large slab–pull force (F_{SP}) acting on the Pacific Plate.

As you will find in Section 2, sea-floor spreading is the dominant means whereby the Earth sheds its internally generated heat energy. Variations in the rate of formation of new oceanic lithosphere, which depends to some extent on the amount of subduction and the influence of the related slab–pull force, imply that other important means of losing this heat must change too.

● Can you think of any other means of heat loss?

● The most obvious is by conduction to the surface, but that, as you will see in Section 2, only accounts for a small and little-varying proportion of heat production. The other means is by convection at hot spots.

● What factor is common to all the forces shown in Figure 1.8?

● They are all ultimately gravitational forces.

Although gravity acts downwards at the surface of the Earth, the differences in elevation, essential for the forces on the plates to have a dynamic effect, stem from differences in temperature, pressure and density within the lithosphere. Any difference in gravitational energy between one point and another is the **gravitational potential energy**.

Gravitational potential energy is the product of mass (volume × density), elevation difference and the acceleration due to gravity. So, by multiplying together mass, height and gravity, you obtain a value for gravitational potential energy. If it can overcome the various resistances to movement, lithosphere will move downslope from high to low gravitational potential, doing work along the way, much as a landslide does, but on a far grander scale.

Although gravitational potential largely drives plate movements, the differences in topographic elevation can result from a variety of processes.

● What is the difference in process of formation of a flood basalt province and a volcanic island arc?

● A flood basalt is the result of extensive eruptions from a hot spot or mantle plume while a volcanic arc is a chain of volcanoes formed by subduction of oceanic lithosphere.

Forces that trend outward from an area of high gravitational potential put the lithosphere under tension. If the lithosphere fails, then within-plate extension takes place. Compression can arise where such forces are opposed. Whether or not differences in gravitational potential energy result in failure and lateral movement of the lithosphere within plates depends on the strength of the rocks involved (Section 3). Blocks 2, 3 and 4 each consider different aspects of these large-scale gravitational processes that work in conjunction with plate tectonics.

1.4   Plate boundaries

This Section reviews some of the processes that occur at plate boundaries, particularly those which deform the lithosphere. Where rocks are cool enough for them to fail in a brittle manner, active deformation occurs along faults, and produces earthquakes. At higher temperatures, rocks deform in an increasingly ductile manner, and movement is not accompanied by seismicity. By definition, plate boundaries are zones of intense seismic activity as plates move relative to one another and overcome resistance in a brittle fashion. The vast majority of large earthquakes occur at one or other kind of boundary, and *all* those deeper than a few tens of kilometres characterize subduction zones, where the descending slab remains cool enough for brittle deformation to depths as great as 600 km or more. Not only has that allowed geophysicists to chart all plate boundaries by recording the location and depth of earthquake foci, but also the nature of the waves received at seismometers gives information about the *type* of motion involved in each major seismic event. By recording whether the first signal to arrive at a seismometer is compressional (an upward movement) or dilational (downward movement), the sense of movement can be determined. This is called a first-motion study.

1.4.1   Constructive margins and continental extension

First-motion studies of earthquakes along ocean-ridge systems indicate two types of faulting: steep normal faults along the ridge axes and vertical strike–slip faults associated with transform faults. These movements are both manifestations of the extensional processes that characterize constructive plate margins. Where partial melting of rising asthenosphere accompanies extension at ridges, the geological outcome is quite simple: the space created by sea-floor spreading is filled by magma.

> **Question 1.3**   Briefly describe the structure of the oceanic lithosphere formed at spreading ridges.

There are complexities associated with transform faults, due to the combined effect of lateral displacement and the subsidence of the lithosphere as it cools and becomes more dense according to the age of oceanic lithosphere away from the ridge (transform faults juxtapose lithosphere of different ages and densities). Occasionally, transform faults 'leak' magma to add a secondary layer of pillow lavas to those formed at the ridge.

Oceans such as the Atlantic began to form where continental lithosphere extended and rifted, much as happened in geologically more recent times to form the Red Sea. In Block 2, you will work with evidence of many kinds to discover how such rifting began, and how the African continent is undergoing extension along the East African Rift System, perhaps separating two continental masses in the future. Because rifted continental margins often become the sites for massive sedimentary deposition as soon as extension begins, their structural 'architecture' becomes quickly obscured. Generally, it is only decipherable from rather blurred images produced by seismic reflection surveys. For the last 30 Ma or so, such continental extension has been taking place on a grand scale in the western USA.

However, due to climatic conditions, sediment deposition there has been slow enough that the structures involved in extension have not been completely obscured.

1.4.2 Destructive margins

Destructive plate boundaries are the graveyards of oceanic lithosphere, because they are where it becomes resorbed into the mantle. Sooner or later, oceanic lithosphere is subducted and that is why there is no ocean floor older than about 170 Ma (Jurassic). At some destructive margins, oceanic crust can become detached and incorporated into continents. Such **ophiolites**, recognizable from their distinctive association of mafic and ultramafic igneous rocks and their veneer of fine-grained sediments that only form in deep ocean basins, are clues to the former existence of destructive margins in ancient orogenic belts. You will encounter one such ophiolite in the Video Band *Forging the land bridge* as part of Activity 4.1 at the end of this Block. Such insights that geologists have into oceanic processes older than 170 Ma come entirely from ophiolites incorporated into continents and island arcs by processes associated with subduction. The lithosphere near Wadati–Benioff zones evolves more quickly and substantially than anywhere else on the planet as new material is continually added because of the opposed plate motions.

As well as being the most intensely seismic zones on Earth, destructive boundaries are the most spectacularly volcanic, both where they form far out into oceans to generate island arcs (Activity 1.1) and where they coincide with continental margins, as in the Andes (Block 3). When an actively spreading oceanic ridge system becomes extinguished by subduction, an ocean starts to close. Unless spreading re-emerges elsewhere in the ocean basin, its margins are destined to collide. Ultimately by this process, two formerly distant blocks of continental lithosphere may coalesce and give rise to mountains, forcing once shallow materials to considerable depths, where they deform and undergo metamorphic change in a complicated manner. Whatever buoyant material once separated such colliding continents, mainly oceanic island arcs but including elevated parts of oceanic lithosphere, it resists subduction and enters the orogenic complex of a continent–continent collision zone. We will return to zones of complex continental welding in Block 4.

Before Earth scientists proposed the theory of plate tectonics, but around the same time that Kiyoo Wadati mapped earthquake foci descending to enormous depths beneath the Japanese islands from the Japan Trench (the 1930s), the Dutch geophysicist Vening Meinesz set out to explain the large gravity variations across trenches and associated arcs, such as those shown in Figure 1.9.

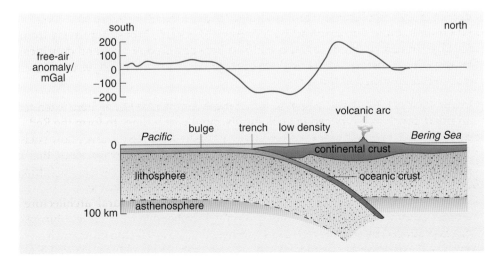

Figure 1.9 Cross-section at right-angles to the destructive plate boundary beneath the Aleutian Islands showing major geological features and the associated free-air gravity anomaly.

forming Activity 4.1 at the end of this Block.

- Locate the Sunda Arc section of Figure 1.10 on DP. What do you think the offshore islands are?

- The islands are not volcanoes, but they are clearly related to the subduction process. They are part of the accretionary prism.

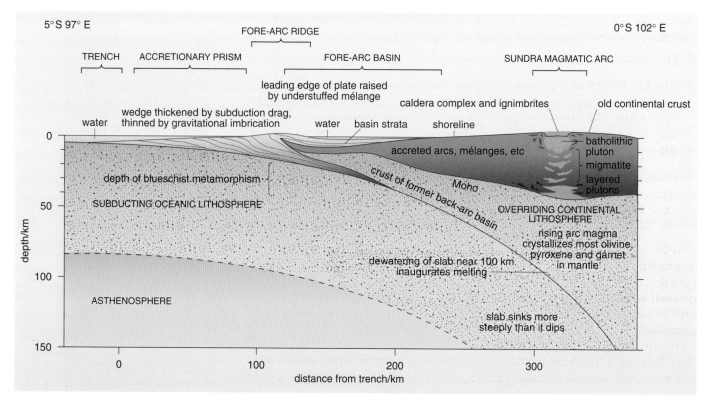

Figure 1.10 Scaled cross-section across the Sunda Arc from 5° S, 97° E (left) to 0° S, 102° E (right).

As the downgoing plate scrapes under the leading edge of the overriding plate, it drives up the surface to create a **fore-arc ridge**, seen in the Sunda Arc as a chain of islands between the trench and Sumatra (Figure 1.10). The rising fore-arc ridge, plus down-flexing of the overriding plate's leading edge, creates a fore-arc basin in which sediments derived from the volcanic arc accumulate.

Consider the materials that form the accretionary prism. Are they all the same age? Do they increase in age downwards in the stack of faulted slices? Or do they increase in age towards the fore-arc ridge? To a first approximation, and since materials are added to the accretionary prism at its leading, oceanward edge, they become progressively younger away from the arc. However, the situation is often more complex than this, as you will discover in Block 3.

Another process is the stuffing beneath the overriding plate of material that escapes addition to the prism at its front, yet fails to be completely subducted. This **tectonic underplating** serves to jack-up overlying material, further increasing the surface slope of the prism towards the trench. Processes at the volcanic part of the arc are the central topic of Block 3. However, both tectonic underplating and addition of new material to the crust by igneous means tend to inflate that part of the arc too, thereby increasing surface slopes. So a stage may well be reached, given time, where the entire crust in an island arc or a volcanic continental margin becomes subject to tensional forces and may fail by gravity-driven extensional processes.

One consequence of prism thickening is that gravity imparts an oceanward force that puts the 'inflated' part of the prism under tension. If it fails, then an extraordinary situation would develop, with extension and compression combined. The young, leading edge of the prism has an unstable surface slope and it continues to be deformed by slice-like imbricate faults, whereas the older, thickened and underplated part extends (Figure 1.10). The material driven beneath the overriding plate succumbs to high-pressure, low-temperature metamorphism. As underplating from beneath adds to these high-P, low-T metamorphic rocks (known as blueschist metamorphism), it drives them upwards with time. This is one possible explanation for the occurrence of such rocks at the sites of ancient subduction zones, where they form the critical evidence for suspecting such a tectonic setting (Block 4).

- ● How does the subduction process stop?

- ● The subduction of the constructive margin that generates the subducted material will stop the process — as in the case of western North America. In such a case, the constructive margin ceases to exist. Subduction may also stop when buoyant lithosphere reaches the subduction zone. Such buoyant lithosphere could be an island arc or a drifting continent.

There are no magnetic anomaly patterns in the Timor Sea to the north-west of Australia, and shallow water extends almost as far as the large, mountainous island of Timor. Lithosphere of the Australian continent has met the Banda Trench. DP shows deep-focus earthquakes either side of the Banda Arc.

Now look at the island of Timor, north of the Timor Sea, which lies in a surprising position, trenchwards of the volcanic arc. Its geology is very different from that expected in a volcanic arc, too. Many of the rocks that comprise Timor are shelf sediments that extend back to the Permian. They are thrust together with at least two ophiolite complexes and high-grade metamorphic rocks. The most likely explanation is that Timor is the former fringe of the Australian continent, that became involved in the main north-north-eastwards subduction zone. Because it could not be subducted, this continental crust thickened, in a similar manner to an accretionary prism, by repeated thrusting. Recent ideas on the evolution of Timor, which stem from detailed seismic sections across the Banda Arc, are illustrated in Figure 1.11.

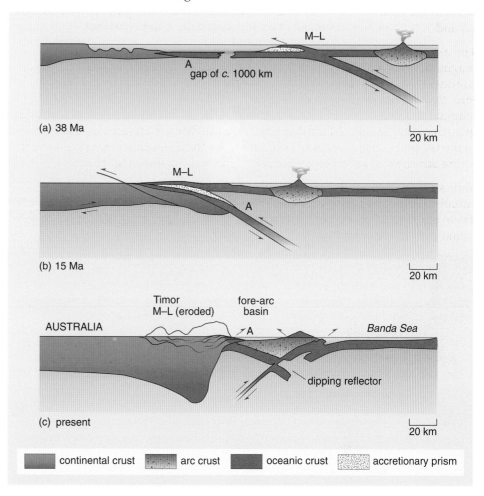

Figure 1.11 Schematic N–S sections across the Banda Arc showing its evolution from 38 Ma to the present, as the Australian lithosphere became involved in subduction. M–L and A are the Mutis–Lolotoi and Aileu ophiolite complexes respectively.

Shelf sediments accumulated on thinned crust on the northern margin of the Australian continent at the flank of a major ocean at 38 Ma (Figure 1.11a). The start of subduction at this time progressively drove Australia closer to the trench and the volcanic-arc system that became the Banda Arc. As Australia reached the trench (Figure 1.11b), thrusting drove oceanic lithosphere onto the continental margin to form an ophiolite (the Mutis–Lolotoi ophiolite, M–L). Further motion north by Australia, driven by spreading of the South-East Indian Ridge, resulted in deformation of its northern margin by thrusting until it reached its present thickened state (Figure 1.11c), to obduct a second ophiolite (the Aileu ophiolite A). This juxtaposed the continental lithosphere of the Australian Plate with the volcanic arc, so that motion could no longer be accommodated by deformation. Subduction has changed direction in the relatively recent past, so that it now proceeds southwards to begin consuming oceanic crust beneath the Banda Sea. Detailed measurements of plate motions show that Timor and the volcanic arc to its north are moving northwards at about 70 mm per year (see DP). Eventually, Timor will 'sweep up' the complex of arcs and continental fragments further to the north.

The destiny of Australasia and this part of the highly complex West Pacific is that a mixture of crustal segments, originating far from each other, will **accrete** to Australia and enlarge its area. Each of the segments should be recognizable from their very different stratigraphical and structural histories. They will constitute distinct **terranes** within the future, enlarged continent. This concept of continental growth by **terrane accretion** is extremely important for modern ideas of how Britain came into being, and in Block 5 the Banda Arc and Timor figure as an analogue for the evolution of Scottish Highland geology. It takes little stretch of the imagination to envisage a similar fate for the simpler arc systems further to the north in the West Pacific — the Mariana, Japanese and Philippine Arcs (Activities 1.1 and 1.2). They may eventually become part of the Asian continent.

The most widespread activity in the plate overriding a subduction zone is magmatic. This manifests itself in the spectacular volcanism of island arcs and continental margins that coincide with plate subduction, such as the 'Ring of Fire' that defines the flanks of the Pacific Ocean. Processes by which this magmatism adds new material which defies later subduction and contributes to growth of the continental crust are discussed in Block 3. Here we examine some of the tectonic consequences of subduction for the lithosphere that rides over it — the **supra-subduction** environment (*supra* is Latin, meaning 'above').

Your study of Activity 1.2 will have revealed the interesting and complex situation at the subduction zone that helps define the Mariana Arc (Figure 1.12). There is a zone of active but slow spreading behind the arc. A similar situation is found behind the Tonga Arc.

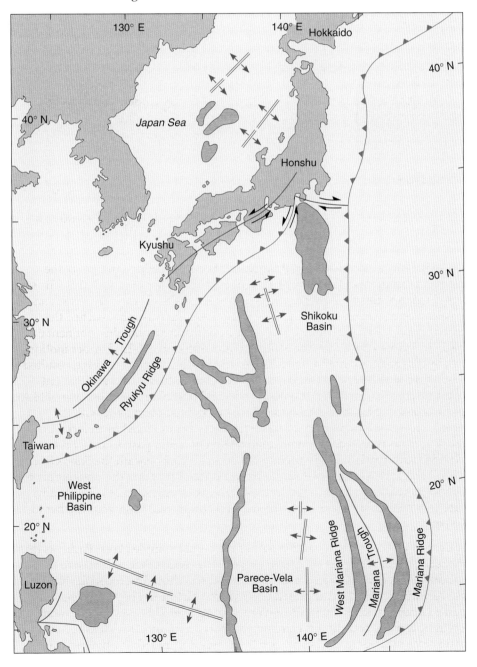

Figure 1.12 Supra-subduction tectonics of the north-western Pacific, showing active subduction zones as blue lines with 'teeth' that point towards the overriding plate. The grey areas are ridges on the ocean floor. Those on the east define a volcanically active arc with small volcanic islands (see DP). Most of the other ridges are thought to be extinct volcanic arcs. The red line in the south-east corner is the active spreading centre that coincides with the Mariana Trough. Double lines with red arrows are features recognized to be former sites of back-arc spreading of this kind.

● What must such **back-arc spreading** signify as regards the tectonics in the supra-subduction environment?

● The lithosphere must be under tension to allow such extensional tectonics.

There is a complex relationship between driving and retarding forces, compressional and extensional tectonics at a destructive plate boundary. An exaggerated cross-section encompassing the Mariana and Ryukyu subduction zones (Figure 1.13) illustrates this point.

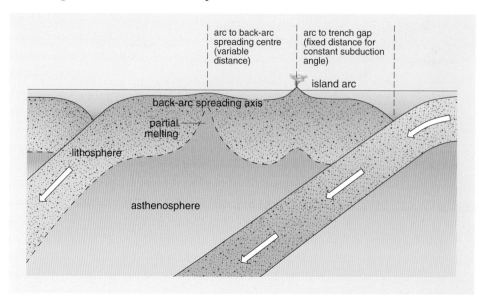

Figure I.13 Exaggerated section across the Mariana and Ryukyu Arcs.

Question I.4 Mark on Figure 1.13 the main driving forces acting on the plates. (a) In this case, which forces are tending to encourage extension? (b) Magma must form beneath the back-arc spreading axis. From where might it rise? (c) Will the back-arc spreading axis remain fixed relative to the subduction zones?

Since the spreading axis moves relative to the subduction zone, it helps explain the presence of extinct back-arc spreading axes. As an axis moves, the process that generates magma to keep such axes active must wane and disappear. The simplest explanation is that back-arc spreading involves a process that occurs at a fixed depth, and thus at a fixed distance from the trench, depending on the angle of subduction.

Regional extensional tectonics behind subduction zones is not confined to the oceanic lithosphere. The Andes, under which the Nazca Plate is being subducted, are influenced by regional extensional tectonics, as you will find in Block 3. However, the most spectacular example occurs in western North America, and involves continental materials; you will study this in detail in Activity 3.1 at the end of Section 3.

1.4.3   Conservative margins

You have already investigated a complex example of a conservative plate boundary in New Zealand during Activity 1.1. There, the Alpine Fault separates two opposed subduction zones, and the Indian Plate is moving north-eastwards relative to the Pacific Plate. This means that most of the North Island and the western part of the South Island are shifting relative to the rest of New Zealand; the New Zealand continental crust fragment consists of two entities that move

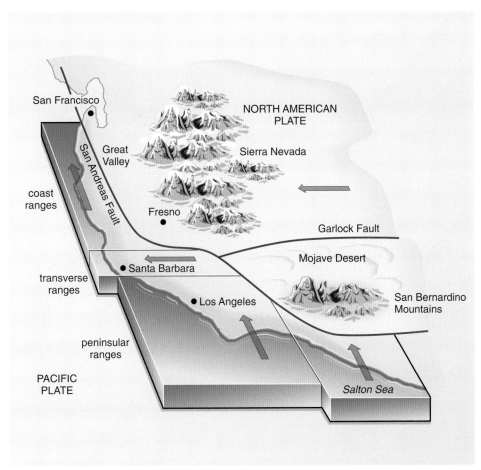

Figure 1.14 Simplified oblique view of the San Andreas Fault system in California. The western blocks are part of the Pacific Plate, and move northwards relative to the North American Plate, which moves westwards, driven by North Atlantic spreading.

with a strike–slip sense across the Alpine Fault. Given time, the two parts may become widely separated. Another example of a conservative plate boundary is the infamous San Andreas Fault of California (Figure 1.14).

Over geologically long periods of time, crustal blocks separated by conservative margins, such as those to the east and west of the San Andreas Fault, become impossible to match in terms of their geological history across the plate boundary; relative to one another, they become increasingly 'exotic'. Both North and South Islands of New Zealand are heading for what are presently subduction zones, and western California will eventually reach the zone of spreading and subduction off Washington State and British Columbia. Probably in both cases the continental slivers will modify other tectonic processes when they arrive. As in the case of island arcs, and colliding continents, accreted head-on to other continental masses, they are destined to become terranes. But rather than resulting from opposed motion, their accretion to continents is by sliding into place laterally. They **dock**, which is quite apposite, because no seafarer comes head on into harbour!

As well as having the best example of continental extensional tectonics, in the form of the Basin and Range Province, western North America is graced with an astonishing dockyard of laterally accreted terranes (Figure 1.15).

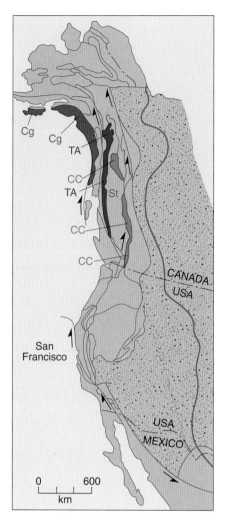

Figure 1.15 Docked terranes of western North America. Those discussed in the text are shown in red: CC Cache Creek; St Stikine; TA Tracey Arm; Cg Chugach. The dark green line shows the eastern limit of Mesozoic to Cenozoic deformation in the North American Plate. Half-headed arrows show directions of strike–slip movement. Stipple indicates the extent of old, pre-accretion continental crust.

Observations that revealed that the western margin of the continent was a composite of the individual terranes shown in Figure 1.15 include:

(i) abrupt discontinuities in rock sequences across major faults, implying very different geological histories in terranes that are now adjacent;

(ii) similar discontinuities in the fossil record (e.g. tropical fossils in displaced terranes are easily distinguished from the cool-temperate forms expected at these latitudes);

(iii) markedly different paleomagnetic characteristics across tectonic boundaries.

Most of the terranes appear to have collided and accreted to the western margin of what is now the North American Plate during Mesozoic and early Cenozoic times. Many originated at great distances from their present position, and may also have moved hundreds of kilometres after accretion. Paleomagnetic evidence indicates significant rotations in many cases. It appears that strike–slip motions on the Pacific border with North America operated throughout the last 100 to 120 Ma. Many of the terranes may even have originated on the far side of the Pacific, as the following evidence shows.

The Cache Creek terrane (CC on Figure 1.15), which is located 300 km inland in western Canada, consists of thick sequences of late Paleozoic, shallow-water limestones deposited directly onto what appears to be oceanic crust. Adjacent to it, on the Pacific side, is the Stikine terrane (St), which comprises Permian to middle Jurassic mafic to felsic volcanic layers and similar volcanogenic sediments; possibly island arc rocks. Succeeding this to the west is the Tracey Arm terrane (TA), a complex of high-grade metamorphic schists and gneisses of unknown age but undoubted continental origin.

● Would you say that the rocks become more oceanic or more continental from east to west?

● The terranes seem to become more continental towards the coast.

There is no clear east–west age trend, although the youngest rocks (Upper Mesozoic to Cenozoic) do occur in the Chugach terrane (Cg), on the Pacific coast around the Canada–Alaska border. Returning to the Cache Creek terrane, the marine sediments contain distinctive marine microfossils known as fusulinids (a family of foraminifer), which date back to the Permian. However, they are totally unlike those occurring further east in the Rocky Mountains, which have always been part of the North American Plate. The fusulinids present in the Cache Creek and other terranes belong to species that occur widely throughout China, Japan, the East Indies and the Malay Peninsula. They also characterize limestones laid down in the ancient Tethys Ocean that lay to the south of the Eurasian continent for much of the Mesozoic, and which closed during the collisions of India with Asia and Africa with Europe in the Cenozoic. It was from the eastern end of Tethys that the present Pacific Ocean began to evolve. This has profound implications for the origin of the Cache Creek terrane.

● How do you think the Cache Creek terrane originated?

● The late Paleozoic limestones of Cache Creek formed part of the ocean floor of Tethys, but must have migrated across the early Pacific, eventually to accrete onto the margin of North America.

This simple but astonishing passage has further implications. The exotic fusulinid-bearing rocks outcrop as much as 500 km inland from the present Pacific coast of North America, implying that all the material to the west of them also originated as displaced terranes.

In a 1980 *Nature* article, Peter Coney and David Jones of the US Geological Survey and University of Arizona, with James Monger of the Canadian Geological Survey, concluded:

> 'During late-Palaeozoic and early-Mesozoic time two-thirds of our planet's surface was paved with an enormous single ocean (Tethys). The other third was Pangea (an all-embracing supercontinent). Assuming that lengths and spacings of spreading centres were similar then to those now, a single large ocean would statistically favour more percentage area of old ocean crust lying around ready to be subducted than at any other time before or since the Phanerozoic. If offshore and/or intra-oceanic arcs correlate with subduction of cold or dense old oceanic crust, as has been suggested, large parts of the late Palaeozoic to early-Mesozoic palaeo-Pacific Ocean could have been festooned with magmatic arcs. As Pangea began to break up and North America began to advance over that ocean, the arcs could have been swept northwards against large sectors of North America's margin to produce most of the Cordilleran mosaic which has been considered here. During this process, the Pacific was cleared of older arcs, oceanic plateaux and continental fragments, leading thus to the creation of the simple plate configuration that characterizes the present eastern Pacific.'

So, the terranes of western North America probably result from 'sweeping clean' the continental fragments of the eastern Pacific. How reasonable is the eloquent theory posed in the last sentence, i.e. how wide was the eastern Pacific?

Question 1.5 We know from the oldest part of the western Pacific that the Pacific Ocean has existed for at least 170 Ma, and spreading rates must have averaged at least 40 mm yr^{-1} during that time. (a) What length of oceanic lithosphere must have been consumed beneath coastal California? (b) Could this oceanic lithosphere have carried fragments of continent that were originally sited on the western side of the Pacific? If so, how? (c) Are the conclusions reached by Coney, Jones and Monger reasonable? Why, in particular, did they suggest that young island arcs had been available for accretion along with older continental fragments?

1.5 Motion in the mantle

If it were possible adequately to summarize in a sentence the processes in the Earth's interior from which all tectonics spring, it would be something like this: 'Hot, ductile mantle rises to be replaced by descending slabs of more rigid, cooler material'. This encompasses the mantle that rises beneath oceanic ridges and hot spots, and the subduction of old, cold oceanic lithosphere, so it is quite satisfying, albeit in a rather superficial way. The main things that it leaves out concern the origin and the fate of the moving material in the mantle. Until quite recently, only conjecture could address such questions. There were two somewhat opposed views: one that the mantle convected from top to bottom in a single set of cells, the other invoking separate motions in the lower and upper mantle with the only common factor being heat transfer from bottom to top. The two features known with certainty were that the rising mantle responsible for hot spots must originate from depths below the lithosphere, because hot spots are fixed relative to plate motions, and that subduction penetrated at least as deep as 600–700 km, from the deepest earthquakes associated with Wadati–Benioff zones. A cartoon showing the general structure of the Earth (Figure 1.16) summarizes the picture and may be familiar to you from a previous course.

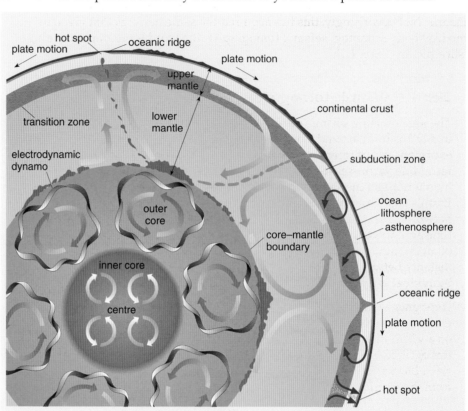

Figure 1.16 Artistic impression of global plate tectonics showing how heat is lost from the Earth by mantle convection.

By analysing seismic data from around the globe, it is possible to deduce the variation in seismic wave speed with depth in the mantle. As well as the asthenosphere, characterized by unexpectedly low speeds, there are two other seismic **discontinuities** in the mantle. Each involves a sudden increase in speed of 3 to 5%, one at about 410 km and the other at around 670 km below the Earth's surface. The generally accepted explanation for these discontinuities is a change in mineralogy in response to increasing pressure. The upper mantle (from 100 to 410 km deep) is mainly olivine–pyroxene–garnet, as revealed by nodules in magmas emanating from these depths. The discontinuity at 410 km probably results from compression of olivine and pyroxene to form a more densely packed molecule or structure, akin to that of spinel. That at 670 km may result from the conversion of all upper-mantle minerals to structures with even denser molecular packing. Laboratory experiments support such hypothetical phase changes at seismic discontinuities in the mantle, and the changes in wave speed are consistent with the measured physical properties of the experimentally produced mineral assemblages.

The coincidence between the deepest earthquakes and the 670 km discontinuity posed something of a dilemma. Geophysicists could account for it either because subducted material ponded at that depth, or because any deeper penetration would involve wholly ductile processes and therefore no seismicity. The first implies separate convection in upper and lower mantle, whereas the second means that convection involves the whole mantle, at least in part. The geochemistry of mantle-derived magmas might seem to hold out a possibility of resolving the dilemma. However, although there are differences between basaltic magmas in various tectonic settings that suggest several mantle reservoirs, such is the complexity of partial melting and magma evolution that the issue is blurred into as many as six possibilities, some hinting at whole-mantle convection, and others at separate upper and lower régimes.

Recent developments that have a bearing on these possibilities stem from the analysis of hundreds of thousands of seismograph records, using supercomputers to model in three dimensions the seismic structure in the mantle. Not surprisingly, this has acquired the same name as that given to medical body scanning: **seismic tomography**, the word tomograph meaning 'slice-picture' (Box 1.1).

Box 1.1 Seismic tomography

The idea of using seismic data as a means of mapping the Earth's interior in 3-D has been around since the mid-1970s. However, it requires enormous computing power to produce results with useful resolution. The technique harnesses the energy emitted by natural earthquakes, and involves much the same principles as the methods used in determining the Earth's gross internal structure. Seismographs from the worldwide network of seismographic stations produce three sets of data: the arrival time and power of different kinds of seismic waves, and the exact location of an earthquake. Plots of arrival time and epicentral angle (the angular distance between an earthquake and a seismographic station) from individual earthquakes give the main clues to Earth structure.

Tomography uses as many seismographic records of an earthquake from as many stations as possible (Figure 1.17). In the same way as a 2-D picture on a video monitor is a regular grid of rectangular picture elements, tomography divides a target volume of the Earth into a number of equal-sized blocks. Each of several seismometers records the energy travelling from the earthquake to a station along a particular 'ray' path. Each source-

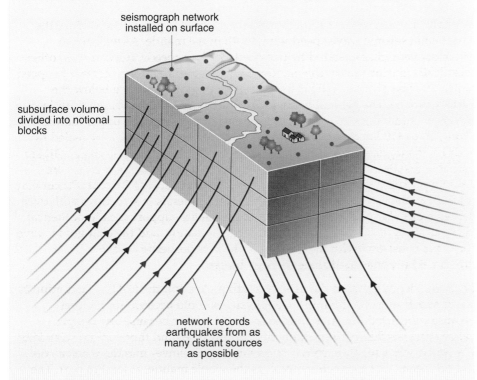

Figure 1.17 Division of the subsurface into blocks, the array of seismometers and the seismic ray paths used in seismic tomography.

to-station path follows a predictable route, so it is possible to know which blocks it passes through. The calculations assume that outside the traversed volume, structure is constant. The computation uses arrival time and path length for each record to detect deviations from the wave speed in each block expected from its depth and the average properties of the mantle. Variations in attenuation of the power of seismic waves along the path length also give information about anomalous properties in each block. The mathematics involves creating a vast number of simultaneous equations, and solving them requires enormous computer power. Reducing the volume of the blocks improves resolution, but as it also increases their number, it also increases the complexity of the calculation. So, the level of detail revealed by seismic tomography evolves with advances in computing speed and digital data storage. The solutions give deviations from the expected wave speed or energy attenuation for each block, in the form of a 3-D array of values that computer graphics can express as images.

Both P- and S-waves are useful in different applications of seismic tomography. Here we are concerned only with deviations from expected wave speed. To understand what the deviations signify means looking at the factors that control seismic-wave speed. P-waves propagate like sound waves as compressions and rarefactions along the wave path. The square of their speed is inversely proportional to the density of the medium and directly proportional to the resistance of the material to compression and expansion. S-waves propagate by displacement of material at right angles to the wave path, to give a shearing motion, for which a very rough analogy is shaking a jelly! The square of the speed of S-waves also decreases with increasing density of rock, and increases as the solid's resistance to shearing — its rigidity — goes up. Mantle rock that is cooler than its surroundings at a particular depth is likely to be more resistant to compression and more rigid than warmer rock. Consequently, cold, descending material will show an unexpectedly high speed, whereas warm, rising mantle should give anomalously low speeds. Because liquids have no rigidity, S-waves will not pass through magma, and zones of partial melting will show very low S-wave speeds.

The resolution of this technique depends on the wavelength of the seismic waves used and the size of blocks used in modelling the data.

Potentially, seismic tomography is capable of mapping the entire mantle, and even features in the Earth's core. However, a word of caution is required when interpreting the images generated from tomographic studies. The following figures are not strictly comparable, as they use different types of data and processing techniques. Any modelling procedure can introduce artefacts that may emphasize or hide real features.

1.5.1 The mantle beneath hot spots

One of the great unresolved conundrums of mantle dynamics is the depth from which the plumes that give rise to hot spots have risen. The fixed position of hot spots relative to movements of the tectonic plates means that the magmatism associated with these plumes must originate beneath the lithosphere, otherwise hot spots would move too.

Although seismically slow regions are more difficult to resolve than fast ones, Figure 1.18 clearly shows deviations in wave speeds for sections through the whole mantle whose mid-point is the Iceland hot spot.

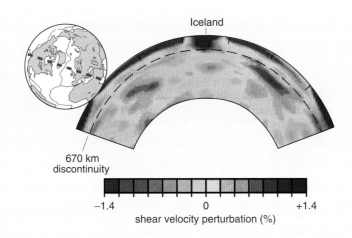

Figure 1.18 Vertical cross-section from S-wave tomography along a great circle that passes through Iceland. The line of the section shows as a red dashed line on the map at left. Ticks on the outer part of the section represent 20° intervals. The dashed black line in the section represents the 670 km mantle discontinuity. As shown in the key to the colours, higher speeds in the tomographic section are 'cool' colours from yellow (no deviation) through green to dark blue, and reduced speeds show as 'warm' colours from yellow to dark red.

> **Question 1.6** Answer (a–c) by using Figure 1.18. (a) What is the velocity structure immediately beneath Iceland? (b) Is there any evidence for a plume in the mantle that extends deeper than 670 km? (c) What features characterize the continental lithosphere shown in the section?

The 'picture' beneath Africa is very different (Figure 1.19). Warm material with low S-wave speed meets the core-mantle boundary beneath South Africa and slopes upwards to the top of the mantle beneath Ethiopia. This zone is very broad, with 'arms' reaching up in several directions. There is obviously warm upwelling material beneath Africa that spans the entire mantle.

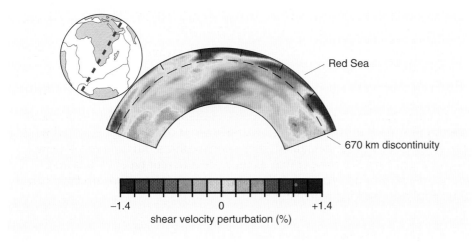

Figure 1.19 Vertical cross-section from S-wave tomography along a great circle from Cape Horn to Arabia. Colours and annotation are the same as in Figure 1.18.

From these two examples, it is clear that hot spots are not necessarily located above plumes that penetrate the whole mantle, but that known in north-east Africa (the Afar hot spot that you will meet in Block 2) certainly does connect to deep mantle upwelling. Yet the zone of warm mantle is neither a narrow 'plume' nor is it rising vertically. Most surprising is that a vast region at the core–mantle boundary is supplying upwelling mantle that appears to move in several directions, most notably towards north-east Africa, but also towards the

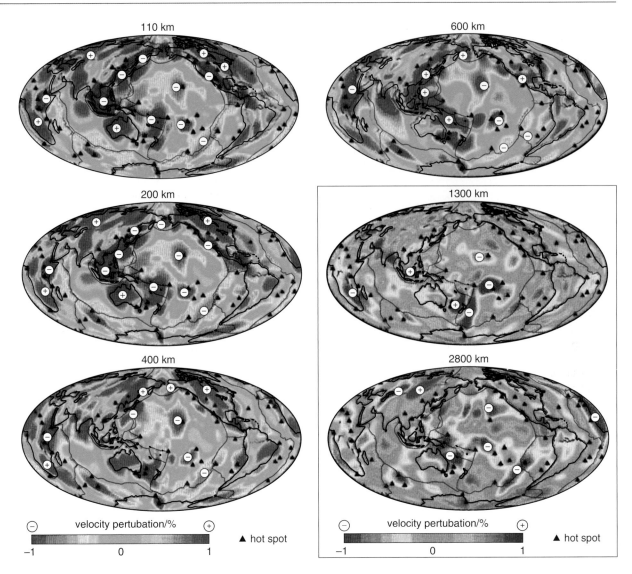

Figure 1.20 Global P-wave tomographic images sliced for six selected depths through the Earth. Red and blue colours denote the slow- and fast-velocity anomalies respectively. Minus and plus signs have been added to key areas to emphasise key regions of slow- and fast-velocity anomalies respectively. Dark lines are continental coastlines and paler lines are tectonic plate boundaries. Note the scalebar on the right is for the two lower mantle slices shown in the box.

Indian Ocean. The variation of P-wave speed with depth for the whole Earth (Figure 1.20) illustrates the differences in the deep structure beneath these hot spots. We will return to this subject using higher-resolution tomography in Section 4.

1.5.2   The mantle beneath destructive margins

An important issue regarding the fate of subducted lithosphere centres on whether it ponds up at the 670 km discontinuity, or passes through it, eventually to bottom-out at the core–mantle boundary. Evidence for the first would tend to support an upper-mantle system of convection decoupled from motions below 670 km, whereas the second possibility implies that convection is mantle-wide. The destructive margin from which you will draw conclusions is that starting at the trench system to the west of Central America. In Central America, the Cocos Plate is subducting beneath the Caribbean Plate at about 60 mm yr^{-1} (see Figure 1.5 and DP).

A vertical section based on P-wave tomography, beginning at the left (south-west) with the Middle America Trench where the Cocos Plate descends beneath Costa Rica, illustrates this apparently simple subduction zone (Figure 1.21).

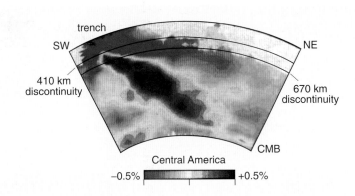

Figure 1.21 Mantle cross-section at right-angles to the Middle America Trench, based on P-wave tomography. Blues represent anomalously high P-wave speeds and cold mantle; reds show low speeds, as shown in the key as a percentage of the expected speed; pale pink to white indicates poorly sampled areas. The section trends north-eastwards from the Middle America Trench into the North Atlantic to just west of the Mid-Atlantic Ridge. Horizontal and vertical scales are the same. CMB is the core–mantle boundary.

It appears (Figure 1.21) that a high-speed feature descends almost to the core–mantle boundary, exactly on line with the dip of the Wadati–Benioff zone of earthquakes above 600 km depth. However, there are two odd features. First, considering the scale of the image — 2900 km from top to bottom and the same horizontal scale — the dipping zone of high P-wave speeds is much wider than subducted lithosphere alone can account for. Upper mantle, cooled by the descending slab, may also be descending. Secondly, the dipping feature begins only at the level of the 410 km discontinuity, and 'slower', warmer mantle drapes over it. There are undoubtedly some artefacts of modelling present here.

Similar high-speed structures dipping steeply to the lower mantle occur in association with several destructive margins, and also below plate margins where subduction has gone on in the past, but has now ceased. The blue feature dipping half-way into the mantle beneath North America (Figure 1.18) may be the relic of subduction of the former eastern Pacific Plate that stopped when the North American Plate overrode the East Pacific Rise and forced it to subduct (see also the answer to Question 1.5). Beneath other active subduction zones, for instance in the north-western Pacific, there are signs that the descending slab deflects at the 670 km discontinuity.

What is becoming clear from whole-mantle seismic tomography is that, at least as far as subduction is concerned, mantle motion penetrates to very deep levels, far below the 670 km discontinuity. In the case of the rising warm mantle beneath Africa, material at that fundamental boundary forms the source for the upwelling. Although this is not the complete picture, whole-mantle convection does seem to dominate the Earth's internal motion.

1.5.3 Deep circulation in the mantle

The weight of tomographic evidence suggests strongly that descending slabs approach the core–mantle boundary. As well as possibly dragging some of the upper mantle down with them (Section 1.5.2), such huge moving masses must also drive material before them; there must be some downward displacement. Since the core–mantle boundary separates ultramafic rock from molten iron–

nickel–sulphur alloys with a very much higher density than any of the mantle, such motion must eventually become lateral at that depth. A cartoon (Figure 1.22) shows the logical consequence of that, displacement of the deepest mantle (and therefore the hottest) into upward motion. The evidence for what goes on beneath Africa (Figure 1.19) suggests that such rising material does not necessarily take the form of a 'well-behaved', narrow plume throughout the entire mantle. Instead it may move in several directions, may not move directly towards the surface, and only in some cases does it take on a classic plume-like form closer to the surface.

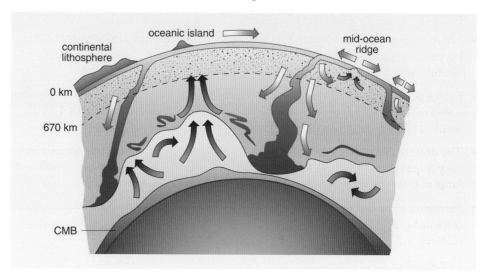

Figure 1.22 A simple model of whole-mantle motion. CMB is the core–mantle boundary.

Question 1.7 Focus on the P-wave velocity structure beneath South Africa in Figure 1.20. Is there any major change in trend above and below the 670 km discontinuity?

There is a wealth of information on the structure and motions within the deep Earth still to be gleaned from seismic tomography. In the following Sections, we will investigate how the mechanical and thermal properties of oceanic and continental lithosphere differ and how they manifest mantle structure and motion.

1.6   Summary of Section 1

- Modern continents have drifted apart over geological time, as revealed by matching margins and similar geological features that occur on continents now separated by major oceans.

- How far some continents have drifted can be gauged from distinctive climatic, and therefore latitudinal, indicators. Rocks containing minerals that preserve remanent magnetization stemming from the Earth's magnetic field when they formed can be used as paleolatitude indicators. Changes of magnetic latitude through time confirm that all continents have drifted.

- Plotting paleolatitudes and directions of remanent magnetization for different periods in the geological evolution of continents produces apparent polar wander paths. Assuming that the Earth's magnetic poles do not wander far relative to its poles of rotation, such plots for pairs of continents give clues to periods when they were united or drifting independently.

- Alternating normal and reversed polarities of the Earth's magnetic field have produced stripe-like magnetic anomalies. Such patterns are roughly symmetrical across oceanic ridges. The anomalies reflect past reversals of the Earth's magnetic field, and can be dated both in continental volcanic rocks and those dredged from the ocean floor.

- The time-scale of oceanic magnetic reversals reveals an increasing age away from active ocean ridges. This is the key to sea-floor spreading that is inseparable from and provides a mechanism for continental drift. Moreover, varying widths of the age-stripes provide an accurate means of judging the rates at which plates move relative to one another.

- The parallelism of chains of Pacific islands and seamounts, formed by passage of the Pacific Plate over a series of hot spots, strongly suggests that the hot spots have remained stationary. If that applies to all hot spots, they form the points of reference for estimating true (absolute) plate movements.

- There are three principal plate boundary types: constructive or divergent plate boundaries, destructive or convergent plate boundaries, and conservative plate boundaries.

- Forces acting on plates involve gravitational effects that induce motion, and various resistive forces that oppose it. A balance between the two sets of opposed forces restricts plate motions to constant speeds.

- The downward pull exerted by subduction of cold dense oceanic lithosphere is very large compared to other plate forces. However, ridge–slide force is sufficiently large to drive plates that have no connection to subduction zones.

- Increased elevation due to the thermal effects of hot spots can reach levels where outward gravitational forces exceed resistive forces. That induces extensional stresses and increased likelihood of the plate failing.

- Constructive plate boundaries are characterized by a magmatically active spreading axis, comprising several spreading centres offset by transform faults. Earthquakes due to extensional faulting characterize spreading centres, while those along active parts of transform faults show strike–slip motions.

- Ophiolites are segments of oceanic lithosphere, built up by igneous rocks sourced by partial melting of mantle materials, together with deep-water sediments that accumulated after mafic–ultramafic lithosphere formed. They are emplaced onto continental crust by tectonic activity.

- At destructive plate boundaries, oceanic lithosphere is subducted into the mantle. Continual subduction accounts for the absence of oceanic lithosphere older than 170 Ma.

- Subduction zones are characterized by deep ocean trenches and by zones of earthquake foci related to the position of a slab of subducting oceanic crust. The dipping seismic zones are called Wadati–Benioff zones.

- Closure of oceans, accretion of island arcs formed in them and the eventual collision of continents that they once separated, result from the subduction of spreading axes, when addition of new material to plates halts. Such accretion of once widely separated terranes adds to the volume of continental lithosphere.

- Overriding plates scrape materials from the upper part of subducting lithosphere, to create accretionary prisms at their leading edges. Such prisms grow trenchwards with the accretion of progressively younger material.

- Tectonic processes beneath overriding plates may stuff part of the subducted slab beneath evolving arcs, thereby imparting increased surface elevation of the arc. Such tectonic underplating, together with magmatic additions, can therefore impart extensional stresses to the developing arc, which can result in failure of the crust.

- Extensional forces above subduction zones manifest themselves by inducing back-arc spreading. Where oceanic lithosphere occurs in the overriding plate, this involves creation of new lithosphere through magmatism at a fixed depth in relation to the subduction zone. Overriding continental lithosphere undergoes extension, exemplified by the Basin and Range Province of western North America.

- Conservative plate margins involve plates moving horizontally relative to one another, requiring faults with dominant strike–slip motions. Where island arcs or continental fragments become associated with such margins, they may eventually meet the margins of larger continental plates, thereby becoming components of laterally accreted complexes of terranes.

- Terranes are fragments of far-travelled lithosphere, separated from others by major faults and displaying strongly contrasted tectonic, stratigraphical and biological histories.

- Mantle discontinuities occur at depths of 410 and 670 km, thought to be due to abrupt changes in density that result from mineralogical phase changes. The coincidence of the 670 km discontinuity with the deepest earthquakes associated with subduction could be due either to completely ductile behaviour of descending slabs below that depth or to their ponding and complete resorption at or above that level.

- Two possibilities for deep mantle motion are (i) that it extends as a single convective system to the core–mantle boundary, and (ii) that it has two components, one above 670 km and another acting independently in the deep mantle.

- Seismic tomography produces 'images' of the mantle that display increased or decreased body-wave speeds relative to those generally expected at different depths. Cool and dense mantle transmits seismic waves at relatively high speeds, whereas warm, lower-density mantle transmits them at slower speeds.

- The mantle beneath hot spots can have various tomographic signatures. The hot spot beneath Iceland has warm low-density mantle extending no deeper than the 670 km discontinuity. The hot spot associated with the Red Sea, on the other hand, has low speed anomalies extending as deep as the core–mantle boundary. So far, there is little evidence for the notion of narrow plumes beneath hot spots, but their origin beneath the lithosphere is confirmed.

- Destructive plate margins are characterized by narrow, high-speed seismic anomalies that extend to the core–mantle boundary, and are best interpreted as descending slabs of cool, dense oceanic lithosphere from active or extinct subduction zones.

- While complex and not yet fully resolved by seismic tomography, convective motion within the Earth seems to be a mantle-wide phenomenon.

Objectives for Section I

Now that you have completed this Section, you should be able to:

1.1   Understand the meaning of all the terms printed in **bold**.

1.2   Identify the geological and geophysical evidence for plate motions.

1.3   Estimate the relative spreading rates of two adjacent plates and describe the absolute movement pattern of any given plate from hot-spot tracks.

1.4   Describe the geological and geophysical parameters that identify and distinguish constructive, destructive and conservative plate boundaries.

1.5   Identify the tectonic processes that are happening at each of the three main types of plate boundary.

1.6   Use data relating to plate boundary lengths, plate areas, the nature of plate boundaries and spreading rates to identify the principal plate-driving forces.

1.7   Recognize and account for anomalies on seismic tomographs.

Now try the following questions to test your understanding of Section 1.

Question 1.8 The theory of plate tectonics requires lithospheric plates to move relative to each other and relative to some fixed global reference frame. What data demonstrate that plates have moved in the past?

Question 1.9 Why do ocean-floor basalts contain magnetic 'stripes'? Why might geoscientists want to study these stripes?

Question 1.10 Why do geoscientists believe the hot-spot reference frame is almost stationary within the Earth? What information does the hot-spot reference frame provide as regards plate movements?

Question 1.11 How do geophysical data from earthquakes help geoscientists to distinguish between different types of plate boundary?

Question 1.12 By ticking the appropriate spaces in the following Table, indicate which of the listed features occur at each different ocean plate boundary type. (Note that some features occur at more than one boundary type.)

Table 1.1   For use with Question 1.12.

Geoscientific feature	Destructive margin	Constructive margin	Conservative margin
Shallow-focus earthquakes (<60 km)			
Deep-focus earthquakes (>60 km)			
Active volcanoes			
Wadati–Benioff zones			
Transform faults			
Offset magnetic stripes			
Magma generation			
Accretionary prisms			
Fracture zones			
Island arcs			

Question 1.13   (a) What is the origin of the slab–pull force that drives plates? (b) Slab–pull is thought to be the most significant plate-driving force, but why can it not be the only one?

2 The engine's power source

The generation and movement of heat within the Earth are the subject of this Section. The tectonic processes described in Section 1 and many of the processes you will encounter in later Blocks occur because of variations in distribution of the Earth's heat. In order to begin to understand these processes, you will need to revise and expand your knowledge of the sources of this heat and its transfer within the Earth.

Lying in the sunshine on a sandy beach close to the Equator, one could be forgiven for thinking that the Earth gets all its heat energy from the Sun. Indeed, solar radiation drives surface processes such as weathering, evaporation and precipitation, and life on Earth is dependent on it. The SI unit of power is the watt (W), defined as 1 joule per second ($J s^{-1}$). About 2×10^{17} W is received at the surface of the Earth from the Sun, most of which is re-radiated into space. Averaged over the whole Earth's surface, this is a power input of about 4×10^2 W m^{-2}. On the other hand, the rate of heat loss from within the Earth is only about 4×10^{13} W or 8×10^{-2} W m^{-2}. Yet, although 10 000 times more solar radiation is reflected at the Earth's surface than heat is lost from within the Earth, it is heat from within that is responsible for all internal processes from the lithosphere to the core. These processes drive plate tectonics and all the associated phenomena: volcanism, metamorphism, earthquakes, intrusions, mountain building, rifting — the list goes on. The reason why internal heat sources are responsible for these processes and not the external solar source is that rocks are very poor thermal conductors. The Sun's heat simply does not penetrate more than a few metres into the Earth. Thus, all the energy dissipated in volcanic eruptions and other shows of strength comes from within the Earth. If you have ever visited deep caves or a mine, you will have noticed that regardless of the weather outside, the temperature below ground is remarkably stable. Daily temperature fluctuations reach only a few tens of centimetres into the crust and surface events that persist over longer time-scales (such as glaciations) only leave a signature that penetrates a few hundred metres at most. This is a very small percentage of the thickness of the Earth's lithosphere and certainly does not affect internal processes within the mantle. Although the heat loss from within the Earth is small compared with heat received from the Sun, the temperature inside the Earth is much higher than at the surface. The rate at which the temperature varies with depth is the **geothermal gradient** or **geotherm**.

The causes and consequences of variations in the value of the geotherm (in time, laterally and with depth) are discussed in this Section. We begin by revising some material that should be familiar to you — the source of heat within the Earth and how the heat is transferred from within the Earth, through the lithosphere to the surface. Next we will look at the differences between oceanic and continental lithosphere in terms of structure and thermal properties, and the implications for mechanical strength in compression and extension.

2.1 Heat transfer

As Flanders and Swan point out in their energy song:

> 'Heat won't flow from a colder to a hotter
> You can try if you want to, but you'd far better notter.'

There are four mechanisms of heat transfer: **conduction, convection, radiation** and **advection**. In every case, energy moves from a higher level to a lower level, and the process by which it does so is different for each mechanism. In the case of *conduction*, heat is transferred from atom to atom or molecule to molecule within a material. The rate at which it does so depends on the temperature gradient — or temperature difference between the hot and cold portions of the material. In the case of *radiation*, photons (electromagnetic radiation) carry away the heat energy from a hotter region to a colder one. In *convection*, matter actually moves, driven by density differences causing buoyancy, taking heat energy with it. Denser (colder) material tends to move downwards, while less dense (hotter) material moves upwards. *Advection* is rather like the upward part of convection; movement of a whole region (e.g. in isostatic rebound) takes heat up with it.

Question 2.1 What factors are important in determining the rate of heat transfer in each of the processes of (a) conduction, (b) convection, (c) radiation and (d) advection?

Question 2.2 How does the Earth's mantle convect in spite of being largely solid? *Hint:* you may remember the concept of Rayleigh number from a previous course.

In the context of heat transfer within the Earth, the most important process is convection. However, before we look at how heat is transported and what its consequences for the evolution of the lithosphere are, we need to consider where the heat comes from.

2.2 Heat generation

Heat is a fundamental feature of the Earth and is generated from six sources. Review these now in Box 2.1 if you are not confident about the significance of the terms 'heat of accretion', 'heat of compression', 'core formation', 'short-lived radioactive isotopes', 'long-lived radioactive isotopes', and 'tidal dissipation' for heat production within the Earth.

Box 2.1 The Earth's heat sources

1 Heat of accretion — the Earth formed by the collision of millions of rocky fragments or planetesimals through a process called accretion. As these fragments accelerated due to gravitational attraction towards the forming Earth, their gravitational potential energy was converted to kinetic ($\frac{1}{2}mv^2$) energy. When they impacted, much of it was then transferred to heat energy. This process caused heating of the Earth and although it is very difficult to quantify, the best estimate is of the order of 10^{32} J.

2 Heat of compression — as a planet grows during formation, the material inside gets compressed whilst new material accretes to the outside. The heat is generated inside the planet and due to the poor heat conduction of rocks, the temperature at depth can increase dramatically. The rate of increase of temperature with depth is the **adiabatic gradient**. For the Earth, the best estimate for the energy due to compression is 2.5×10^{32} J.

3 Core formation — the Earth has differentiated to form a dense core surrounded by a relatively lower density mantle and even lower density crust. Assuming that accretion involved homogeneous materials, the material that now forms the core needed to migrate there. It would have sunk towards the centre under the influence of gravity because of its relatively high density. The conversion of gravitational potential energy by this dense material accounts for approximately 10^{31} J of heat energy.

4   Short-lived radioactive isotopes — in this context, radioactive isotopes with a half-life of 10^6 years or less are considered to be short-lived because this is a short time compared with the age of the Earth. When material containing short-lived radioactive isotopes (formed in a supernova that may have triggered Solar System formation) was accreted into the Earth during formation, the energy released during decay would become trapped within the Earth. About 10^{32} J of heat would have been produced for the first few million years of the Earth's existence from this source.

5   Long-lived radioactive isotopes — radioactive isotopes with half-lives much longer than 10^6 years contributed a relatively small amount of heat energy (up to 10^{29} J) during Earth formation, but they are still important today. The most important isotopes in this context are uranium (^{238}U), thorium (^{232}Th) and potassium (^{40}K). During accretion, this source would have generated 10^{28}–10^{29} J.

6   Tidal dissipation — the relative motions of the Sun and Moon cause the solid Earth (as well as the oceans and atmosphere) to deform in response to the varying gravitational pull. The movement is thought to amount to about 10^{25} J per million years at present. It would have been much greater when the Earth was younger as the Moon was then closer to Earth.

With the exception of long-lived radioactive isotopes, these sources of heat were important during formation of the Earth. At present, although core formation may still be active and tidal dissipation certainly is, the most significant contribution to heat production within the Earth is from long-lived radioactive isotopes. By making estimates of the amount of heat-generating isotopes likely to be within the Earth, it is possible to estimate the amount of heat production.

●   Are the heat-generating isotopes likely to be uniformly distributed throughout the Earth?

●   The Earth is not homogeneous because it has differentiated, with the **siderophile**, dense material sinking into the core and the **lithophile** material concentrating in the mantle and crust. Heat-generating isotopes are lithophile and are therefore concentrated in the mantle and crust.

These heat-producing elements are present in the crust in small quantities, parts per million in the cases of uranium and thorium and parts per hundred for potassium. However, as you will see when you have completed Table 2.1, the **heat generation** is substantial.

Activity 2.1

You should now attempt Activity 2.1 which will help you to revise the material you have covered so far in this Section and take you through a simple calculation that will enable you to complete Table 2.1. You should take about 30 minutes to do this Activity.

Table 2.1 Typical concentrations and heat productions of radiogenic elements with rock types. For use with Activity 2.1.

	Granite	Tholeiitic basalt	Alkali basalt	Peridotite	Average upper continental crust	Average oceanic crust	Mantle
Concentration by weight							
U (ppm)*	4	0.1	0.8	0.006	1.6	0.9	0.02
Th (ppm)	15	0.4	2.5	0.04	5.8	2.7	0.10
K (%)	3.5	0.2	1.2	0.01	2.0	0.4	0.02
Heat generation (10^{-10} W kg^{-1})							
U	3.9	0.1	0.8	0.006	1.6	0.9	0.02
Th	4.1	0.1	0.7	0.010	1.6	0.7	0.03
K	1.3	0.1	0.4	0.004	0.7	0.1	0.007
Total	9.3	0.3	1.9	0.020	3.9	1.7	0.057
Density (10^3 kg m^{-3})	2.7	2.8	2.7	3.2			
Heat generation (μW m^{-3})**	2.5	0.08	0.5	0.006	1.0	0.5	0.02
Total heat generation (μW)	–	–	–	–			

*ppm = parts per million. It is similar in concept to %, which is 'out of a hundred'; ppm means 'out of a million'.
**μW m^{-3} is microwatts per cubic metre (μ means 'millionth of', or 10^{-6}).

Having completed Activity 2.1, it should be clear that the thermal contributions from uranium and thorium are greater than that of potassium and that about a fifth — or 20% — of the Earth's radiogenic heat production occurs within the crust. It should also be clear that granite (typical of upper continental crustal rock) has a greater internal heat generation capacity for a given mass than mafic igneous rocks (typical of oceanic crust). Thus, oceanic lithosphere has less heat generation than continental lithosphere.

It is fascinating to speculate on how heat flow may have varied over geological time as the relative importance of the other heat-producing mechanisms changed. Clearly, an understanding of this variation is essential to the development of models for tectonic processes in the early Earth. However, for now we shall restrict ourselves to a consideration of the present day — which is quite complicated enough! We shall consider next how temperature varies with depth in the lithosphere.

2.3 Thermal gradients in the Earth

The temperature of a rock depends upon many internal and external factors. It depends on the depth at which it is buried, the ability of the rock to dissipate heat (related to thermal diffusivity), its specific heat capacity and its density. Temperature also depends on the heat generation within and below the rock and the rate of erosion (or deposition) above it. The rate at which temperature varies with depth is the geothermal gradient. As the dominant processes of heat flow vary with depth, as we shall see later, the geothermal gradient changes with depth too. If the rate of heat input (from within and below) is balanced by heat output, then temperature will remain constant for any given depth and the temperature–depth relationship will be a **steady-state geotherm**. The relationship of temperature with depth for a simple one-layer model 50 km thick is shown in Figure 2.1.

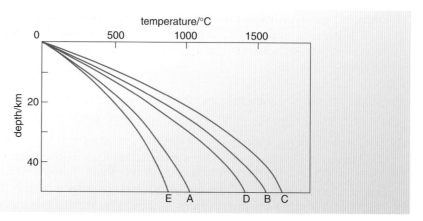

Figure 2.1   Steady-state geotherms for a 50-km-thick rock column using a single-layer model. Each curve represents the temperature at depth for slightly different assumed parameters. A conductivity $2.5 \, W \, m^{-1} \, °C^{-1}$, heat generation $1.25 \, \mu W \, m^{-3}$ and heat flow from below $21 \times 10^{-3} \, W \, m^{-2}$; B conductivity $1.7 \, W \, m^{-1} \, °C^{-1}$, heat generation $1.25 \, \mu W \, m^{-3}$ and heat flow from below $21 \times 10^{-3} \, W \, m^{-2}$; C conductivity $2.5 \, W \, m^{-1} \, °C^{-1}$, heat generation $2.5 \, \mu W \, m^{-3}$ and heat flow from below $21 \times 10^{-3} \, W \, m^{-2}$; D conductivity $2.5 \, W \, m^{-1} \, °C^{-1}$, heat generation $1.25 \, \mu W \, m^{-3}$ and heat flow from below $42 \times 10^{-3} \, W \, m^{-2}$; E conductivity $2.5 \, W \, m^{-1} \, °C^{-1}$, heat generation $1.25 \, \mu W \, m^{-3}$ and heat flow from below $10.5 \times 10^{-3} \, W \, m^{-2}$.

● For the model shown in Figure 2.1, what is the effect on the geothermal gradient of varying the basal heat flow?

◑ For higher basal heat flows (e.g. $42 \times 10^{-3} \, W \, m^{-2}$; curve D), the geothermal gradient at shallow levels is increased. For lower basal heat flows (e.g. $10.5 \times 10^{-3} \, W \, m^{-2}$; curve E), the geothermal gradient at shallow and deep levels is decreased. For a medium basal heat flow (e.g. $21 \times 10^{-3} \, W \, m^{-2}$; curve A), the geothermal gradient at deep levels is increased relative to the lower heat flow model, but is decreased at shallow and deep levels relative to the higher heat flow model.

Unfortunately, life is never simple and the heat flow in the Earth cannot be modelled beyond a first approximation in terms of a single uniform layer. The next most simple model consists of two layers. The maths is only a little more complicated here and the important point is that the basal heat flow into the bottom of the overlying layer is the heat flowing out of the top of the underlying layer. Both layers can have different contributions from internal heat generation. A model calculated for Archean crust is illustrated in Figure 2.2. The upper and lower layers have a radioactive heat generation of $4.2 \, \mu W \, m^{-3}$ and $0.8 \, \mu W \, m^{-3}$ respectively, while the heat flow into the lower layer is $63 \times 10^{-3} \, W \, m^{-2}$.

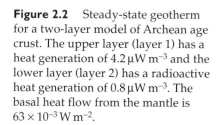

Figure 2.2   Steady-state geotherm for a two-layer model of Archean age crust. The upper layer (layer 1) has a heat generation of $4.2 \, \mu W \, m^{-3}$ and the lower layer (layer 2) has a radioactive heat generation of $0.8 \, \mu W \, m^{-3}$. The basal heat flow from the mantle is $63 \times 10^{-3} \, W \, m^{-2}$.

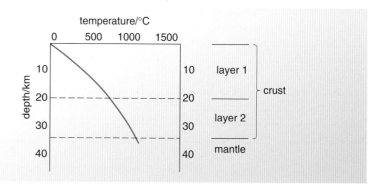

● Assuming that the values chosen for heat generation and basal heat flow are reasonable, what conclusion could you draw from the differences between the steady-state geotherms in Figures 2.1 and 2.2?

● The rate of increase of temperature with depth is rather greater in Figure 2.2 than in Figure 2.1 (except for the most extreme cases illustrated in Figure 2.1). If the assumptions put into these models are reasonable, then this suggests that Archean crust may have been relatively hot compared with present-day crust.

● What would the geotherm look like if the surface temperature of the Earth were say 400 °C, as on Venus, rather than closer to 0 °C on average?

● Temperature would increase with depth at the same rate as it does now, as that increase depends on the mass and density distribution and not on surface temperature. However, it would start 400 °C hotter and so would be hotter at shallow depths. This implies shallower melting than on the real Earth and would have implications for lithosphere thickness, as we shall see later.

The thermal properties of rock are responsible for the thermal behaviour of the Earth. Rock has a relatively high **specific heat capacity** (a measure of the amount of energy needed to increase the temperature of 1 kg of a material by 1 K). In contrast, rock typically has a rather low **thermal conductivity** (a measure of the transfer rate of heat). As an illustration of the range and typical values of specific heat capacity and thermal conductivity, Table 2.2 shows approximate values for some general rock types and common materials.

Table 2.2 Comparison of specific heat capacity and thermal conductivity for some general rock types and common, everyday materials.

Material	Thermal conductivity, $W\,m^{-1}\,K^{-1}$	Specific heat capacity, $J\,kg\,K^{-1}$
Upper mantle	2–3	1.8×10^3
Upper continental crust	1–5	1.5×10^3
Oceanic crust	1–2	1.4×10^3
Water	0.6	4.2×10^3
Copper	400	3.9×10^2

This means that it takes a huge amount of energy to heat up rock; and when it is hot, it does not give up its heat again quickly. Rocks are therefore good insulators, as anyone who has used a barbecue pit knows. These factors make our job of trying to understand the thermal history of the Earth rather difficult. The measurement of heat flow is needed for investigations of the thermal history of the Earth and to develop models for the internal transfer of the Earth's heat in the past, present and future. All we can actually do is measure the present-day temperature at several locations on the face of the Earth down to depths of, at most, a few km. From these measurements (of which there are more than 25 000 worldwide, mostly made on land), we try to infer the temperature in the rest of the Earth. Given the problems in making temperature and depth measurements, this is a tall order. Moreover, the very act of drilling a probe to measure temperature raises the temperature within the borehole whilst circulation of drilling fluids reduces the temperature. This effect can be reduced by waiting for a while before the measurement is made, but the material is nevertheless disturbed by the friction of the drill and the cooling of the drilling fluid.

Heat flow is calculated by multiplying together the average thermal conductivity (often measured *in situ*, or sometimes on a range of recovered samples from the borehole) and the thermal gradient. In addition to measurement errors, local topography and sedimentation or erosion must be taken into account. For continental samples, short- and long-period surface temperature changes (daily, e.g. sunshine, to thousands of years, e.g. glaciations) affect the measurements down to depths of one to hundreds of metres respectively. All these problems can be overcome to varying degrees and heat flow measurements have been made successfully at marine and continental locations. Simple models have been developed to explain the variations in heat flow observed. We shall look at some of these in the following Sections.

2.4   Oceanic heat flow

Sea-floor heat flow is highest in areas of young lithosphere and decreases with distance from spreading ridges. There is considerable variability in the data (Figure 2.3), but models that have been developed to account for the observations are consistent with the key features of plate tectonics (reviewed in Section 1.3). No model fits the observations perfectly because models inevitably contain simplifications and approximations. The difference between three of the models and the data points are clear in Figure 2.3.

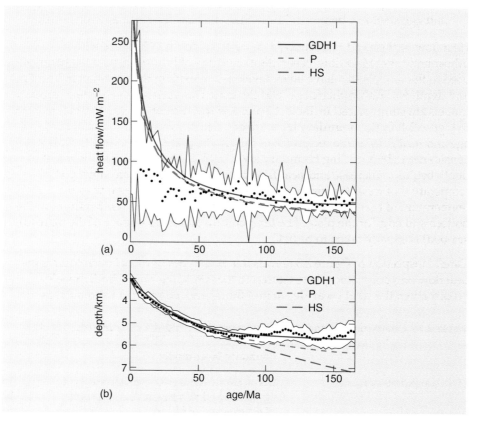

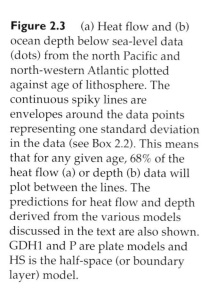

Figure 2.3   (a) Heat flow and (b) ocean depth below sea-level data (dots) from the north Pacific and north-western Atlantic plotted against age of lithosphere. The continuous spiky lines are envelopes around the data points representing one standard deviation in the data (see Box 2.2). This means that for any given age, 68% of the heat flow (a) or depth (b) data will plot between the lines. The predictions for heat flow and depth derived from the various models discussed in the text are also shown. GDH1 and P are plate models and HS is the half-space (or boundary layer) model.

⬤ Are heat flow data most variable close to spreading ridges or further away?

⬤ The heat flow data are much more scattered for ages of 0–30 Ma (younger lithosphere, closer to the spreading ridge). For older lithosphere, further from the spreading ridge, the data are much less scattered.

Box 2.2 Normal distribution and standard deviation

A **normal distribution** of data is one where an equal number of
observations fall above and below the mean. The distribution is also
symmetric, like a bell, in that very few observations fall far away on either
side and most fall close to the mean. For a normal distribution, the
standard deviation is an important value as it provides information on the
shape of the distribution (whether the bell is very tall and thin (small
standard deviation) or short and fat (large standard deviation)). One
standard deviation is defined as the range about the mean within which
68% of the data fall. Two standard deviations about the mean encompass
95% of the data. The envelope in Figure 2.3 represents one standard
deviation. Where the envelope is wide, the standard deviation is large and
this is an indication that the uncertainty (spread) of the data is large. You
will encounter standard deviation again in Activity 2.2, and again in
Block 3.

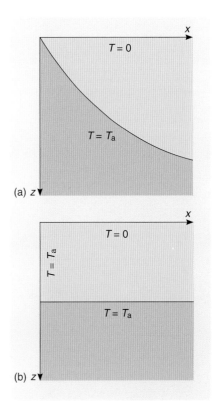

🔘 Why are the depth data not so scattered?

🔘 The uncertainties involved in making depth measurements are much
smaller than the uncertainties involved in heat flow measurements. There is
also more genuine variability in heat flow. The relationship between depth
and age seems to be more simple than the heat flow and age relationship.

Heat flow is observed to decrease and sea-floor depth to increase with
lithospheric age. Heat flow, ocean depth and age of lithosphere are the parameters
used in the models that have been developed to explain the variation in heat flow
and depth with lithospheric age, and the main characteristics of some of the best
models are summarized in Table 2.3 along with cartoons of their thermal features
in Figure 2.4. In the **boundary layer model**, depth varies with the square root of
age and heat flow as the reciprocal of this. In the **plate model**, the lithosphere is
considered to be a cooling boundary layer until it reaches an age at which the
depth begins to increase and heat flow begins to decrease more slowly. The
temperature of the asthenosphere (T_a) is considered to be the same as the
temperature of rising material at the ridge axis; these are the temperatures of the
bottom and edge of the plate. The temperature of the top surface of the plate (the
sea-bed) is usually taken to be $0\,°C$.

Figure 2.4 Schematic cartoon of (a)
the boundary layer model and (b) the
plate model of oceanic lithosphere.
Yellow region is lithosphere and
orange region is asthenosphere. T_a is
temperature of the asthenosphere
boundary.

Careful inspection of Figure 2.3 reveals that both types of model overestimate the
heat flow on young lithosphere (closest to the spreading ridge). Both models
predict about the right ocean depth for lithosphere younger than about $70\,Ma$.

Table 2.3 Comparison of the boundary layer model and the plate model.

	Boundary layer model	Plate model
Main predictions of model	Ocean depth varies with the square root of age and heat flow varies as the reciprocal of the square root of age	The lithosphere behaves as a cooling boundary layer of constant thickness until it reaches a certain age, at which it begins to cool more slowly due to increased plate thickness
Observation for younger oceanic lithosphere	Model is consistent with heat flow and depth data; in addition, seismic data show the lithosphere thickens away from the ridge axis in a similar way to that predicted by this model	Model is consistent with heat flow and depth data
Observation for older oceanic lithosphere	Model is not consistent with observed levelling out of depth with ages above about $100\,Ma$ (see Figure 2.4b)	Preferred model for ages above about $70\,Ma$ as it agrees better with observations of both heat flow and depth

For older lithosphere the plate model is slightly better than the boundary layer model because it assumes that the rate of plate thickening (and hence cooling) will start to level off.

There are variants of the plate models, and two examples of plate models are compared in Table 2.4. The **Global Depth and Heat flow model** (GDH1) actually predicts heat flow on oceanic lithosphere aged up to 1 Ma to be 1020 mW m^{-2}, but the highest observed heat flow on this age range is less than 250 mW m^{-2}. However, of the various plate models, GDH1 fits the observed data rather better than other models after 70 Ma.

Table 2.4 Parameters used for the plate models illustrated in Figure 2.3. You do not need to remember the equations or data used here.

Property	Plate model GDH1	Plate model P
Plate thickness	95 km	125 km
Heat flow (q) with age (t, Ma) relationship	$q(t) = 510\, t^{-0.5}$ mW m^{-2} for ages up to 55 Ma	$q(t) = 473\, t^{-0.5}$ mW m^{-2} for ages up to 120 Ma
Heat flow with age assumption	A more complex function of temperature for ages greater than 55 Ma	A more complex (different from GDH1) function of temperature for ages greater than 120 Ma
Basal temperature	1450 °C	1350 °C
Thermal expansion coefficient	3.1×10^{-5} °C^{-1}	3.28×10^{-5} °C^{-1}
Thermal conductivity	3.138 W m^{-1} °C^{-1}	3.138 W m^{-1} °C^{-1}
Specific heat	1.171 kJ kg^{-1} °C^{-1}	1.171 kJ kg^{-1} °C^{-1}
Mantle density	3330 kg m^{-3}	3330 kg m^{-3}
Water density	1000 kg m^{-3}	1000 kg m^{-3}
Ridge depth	2600 m	2500 m

The Global Depth and Heat flow plate model (GDH1) for oceanic lithosphere is actually a hybrid model as it uses the heat flow and depth relationship assumptions of the half-space model up to ages of 55 Ma (Table 2.4). The fact that depth does not continue to increase with age after about 65 Ma suggests that conduction is not the only mechanism for heat transport. It is now believed that there is convective replacement of cold material by hotter material beneath the base of an old plate and that this maintains the basal isotherm of 1450 °C at 95 km (Table 2.4). These figures are not precise, and may yet be revised. Until recently, the figures of 1350 °C and 125 km (Table 2.4) were favoured. The fact that the Global Depth and Heat flow model fits the data better suggests that oceanic lithosphere is thinner and hotter at depth than was previously thought. Figure 2.5 illustrates the probable thermal structure beneath ocean basins.

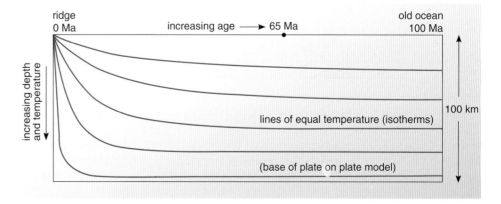

Figure 2.5 The temperature distribution within oceanic lithosphere according to the best-fitting plate model.

⬤ What do the shapes of the curves in Figure 2.5 tell you about heat transfer in oceanic lithosphere according to the plate model?

⬤ The curves suggest that apart from at the very edge of the plate, temperature increases smoothly with depth and there is no lateral variation in temperature. This is consistent with conductive heat transfer.

Question 2.3 What would you expect the geotherm to look like (a) within oceanic lithosphere depicted by the plate model and (b) below it?

According to the plate model, heat flow is conductive through the oceanic lithosphere. The rate of change of temperature with depth is therefore gradual and linear. Below this region, heat transport is largely by convection and the geotherm is much less steep when viewed with temperature as the vertical axis (Figure 2.6). The base of the oceanic lithosphere is defined as the intersection between these two regimes. It is the depth at which the **convective geotherm** meets the **conductive geotherm**. Another definition of the oceanic lithosphere is the rigid outermost skin of the Earth overlying a plastic asthenosphere. The junction between these two mechanically distinct regions is not a sharp boundary, but a transition zone characterized by viscous behaviour. This transition region is able to flow and thus be yielding, like the plastic layer beneath it, but it also has a strong resistance to flow (much like cold porridge). The concept of the outermost layer being mechanically rigid has led to use of the term **mechanical boundary layer**. This layer lies between the surface and the depth to an isotherm (say T_1) that represents the transition from rigid (above) to viscous (below) behaviour. This isotherm and a deeper one (at T_2) define the limits of the transitional layer, which is connected physically to the mechanical layer and moves along with it, yet which is capable of independent internal convective movement. It has become known as the **thermal boundary layer** (Figure 2.6).

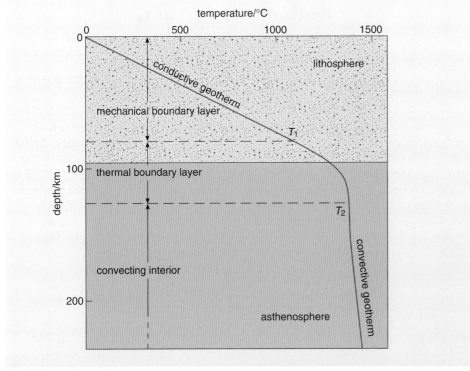

Figure 2.6 The geotherm of oceanic lithosphere as predicted by the plate model. Oceanic lithosphere consists of a rigid mechanical layer characterized by a conductive geotherm and the upper part of a thermal layer attached by viscous drag to the asthenosphere in the region of transition between conductive and convective heat transfer.

The thermal boundary layer represents the transitional region between the heat-conducting mechanical boundary layer above and the convecting mantle beneath. It is therefore not surprising that the rate of change of temperature with depth, or *geotherm*, is curved in this region (Figure 2.6). The exact degree of curvature will depend on the viscosity and therefore thickness of the thermal boundary layer.

Both plate and half-space models overestimate the heat flow for young lithosphere. This is thought to be due to the result of heat being advected away from young oceanic crust by seawater penetrating the porous volcanic and sedimentary rocks of the oceanic crust. The models assume that heat is transported only through conduction. If it is correct that seawater penetration produces the discrepancy between the observations of heat flow and the predictions of the model, then it should be possible to determine the age at which the lithosphere effectively becomes sealed by noting a decrease in difference between the observations and predictions. This is the age beyond which the main heat flow is through conduction. Sealing is probably due to some combination of processes involving sedimentation of clays (causing a barrier), deposition of minerals into fractures and pore spaces and closure of pores by water pressure (decreasing the porosity and permeability).

Activity 2.2

You should now attempt Activity 2.2. This will help to consolidate what you have learnt in this Section and enable you to deduce the sealing age for oceanic lithosphere. You should take about 30 minutes to do this Activity.

The hydrothermal circulation in oceanic crust has important implications for the chemistry of the oceans. This is because seawater reacts with the crust, giving rise to hydrothermal fluid of a very different composition from that of unreacted seawater. The largest effects result from high-temperature water flow at the ridge axis but, as you have discovered in Activity 2.2, sealing is not complete until about 65 Ma and so some reaction occurs even in crust a few tens of millions of years old. Some chemical reactions between seawater and anhydrous minerals in basalt actually generate heat. These are **exothermic** reactions. Thus, hydrothermal circulation can both cool down and heat up oceanic lithosphere.

We are now in a position to draw up a model for oceanic lithosphere. It is homogeneous, without vertical or horizontal zonations. The results obtained in Activity 2.2 indicate that oceanic lithosphere older than about 65 Ma has a higher heat flow than predicted by the models. Possible ways in which the heat flow at the base of the lithosphere could remain higher than expected for older oceanic lithosphere are (i) shear stress heating caused by a differential motion between the lithosphere and asthenosphere, (ii) increased heat production in the upper mantle in these regions, (iii) exothermic chemical reactions in the crust and (iv) small-scale convection in the asthenosphere at the base of older lithosphere. The last possibility is the most likely and would increase the heat flow into the base of the rigid lithosphere and maintain a constant lithosphere thickness. The lithospheric plate is therefore thought to consist of an upper rigid layer and a lower viscous thermal layer (Figure 2.7).

Figure 2.7 Schematic cartoon of the oceanic lithosphere, showing the mechanical boundary layer overlying the thermal boundary layer. Thermal instability occurs at about 60 Ma and convection cells form in the thermal boundary layer, allowing heat flow to fall off less rapidly with age than would otherwise be the case.

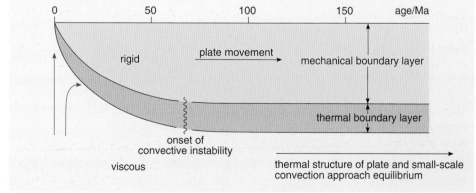

At about 60 Ma, this layer becomes unstable and small-scale convection develops within it. This gives rise to higher heat flow than would otherwise occur and a lithospheric thickness that does not increase further.

2.4.1 Heat flow away from the spreading axis

It is not altogether surprising from what you know of plate tectonics that heat flow is highest along a spreading axis and that it decreases with distance from the axis. But what are the characteristics of heat flow at other features of oceans such as regions of back-arc spreading, subduction zones and at accretionary prisms?

You may recall from your observations of the Pacific region in Activity 1.1 that measurements made in the western Pacific indicate that (i) heat flow decreases with distance from the spreading axis, (ii) heat flow is low between the axis of the trench and the volcanic arc and (iii) heat flow is high and variable over the volcanic zone. Heat flow in the back arc is comparable with heat flow in the major oceanic basins for lithosphere of the same age. The depths of the marginal basins though are up to 1 km deeper for their age than predicted by the models. This may be due to more efficient heat removal and to upper mantle convection associated with back-arc spreading.

Accretionary prisms are characterized by water-saturated sediments known as turbidites that pour into trenches. Heat flow in these provinces is extremely variable and may be due to the migration of pore fluids in a process similar to the one operating at spreading ridges through the hydrothermal system.

Hot spots of course produce an anomalously high signal in the heat flow regime of oceanic lithosphere. As you will remember from Section 1.2, the Hawaiian islands are the surface manifestation of a mantle plume. The island chain tracks the progression of the oceanic lithosphere as it has crossed the plume. The ocean floor around the plume head — called the Hawaiian swell — is characterized by shallower depth than expected for lithosphere of comparable age. However, heat flow is hardly any higher in this region than predicted by the Global Depth and Heat flow plate model. The same is observed for other hot spots, and the swell without anomalous heat flow increase is thought to be due to the dynamic effect of the upwelling mantle rather than thermal expansion in the lithosphere. This is consistent with seismic data, which show no evidence of a low-velocity (e.g. melting) zone beneath the Hawaiian swell.

2.5 Continental heat flow

Continental lithosphere is more varied in terms of its composition, its thickness and its tectonic history than oceanic lithosphere. For these reasons, there is no simple age/heat flow relationship as there is for oceanic lithosphere. The biggest difference is that due to its composition. Radioactive heat production can be substantial in continental crust, especially in its upper parts. Heat flow in continental lithosphere therefore depends on the amount of surface crustal radioactivity and the length of time since the last major tectonic event. Different places have different characteristics and these are termed **heat flow provinces**. For example, England and Wales form one heat flow province whereas the United States is divided into several separate provinces. Data from several different heat flow provinces are plotted on Figure 2.8.

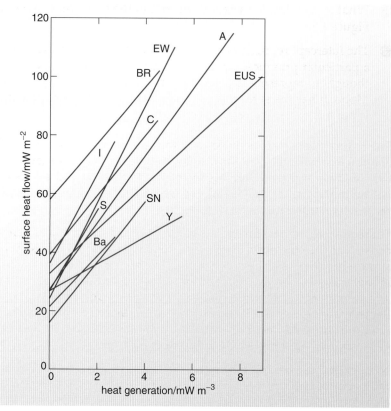

Figure 2.8   Surface heat flow and heat generation for a range of heat flow provinces. A Central Australia; Ba Baltic shield; BR Basin and Range province; C Atlantic Canada; EW England and Wales; EUS Eastern USA; I India; S Superior province, USA; SN Sierra Nevada; Y Yilgarn block, Australia.

For each province, the relationship between surface heat flow and heat generation in Figure 2.8 is a straight line.

● Can you recall the simple equation which describes a straight line?

● It is an equation of the form $y = mx + c$, where y is the value on the vertical axis (the ordinate), and x is the value on the horizontal axis (the abscissa), m is the gradient of the line and c is the value of the intercept on the y-axis (where $x = 0$).

● Give the variable on the vertical axis the symbol q_s for surface heat flow, the variable on the abscissa A for heat generation, the gradient the symbol d and the intercept the symbol q_r. Can you write down an equation to describe the relationships in Figure 2.8?

● The relationship is $q_s = dA + q_r$.

Continental heat flow provinces are differentiated by having different values for q_r, d and A in Equation 2.1:

$$q_s = dA + q_r \tag{2.1}$$

where q_s is surface heat flow (mW m^{-2}), d is the gradient and A is radioactive heat production. The intercept q_r is called the **reduced heat flow**. The units of d are metres and we shall consider its significance in more detail in a moment.

Each line in Figure 2.8 represents data from a different heat flow province. The intercept (q_r) is different for each province.

● What do you think is the significance of the value of q_r, the intercept in Figure 2.8?

● The intercept represents a background heat flow that is always present for a particular province, whatever the value of total heat generation. It is thought to represent the heat flow from deep crustal regions or at the Moho. It has the same value everywhere within a heat flow province, but is not necessarily the same for adjacent provinces.

The reduced heat flow is uniform within a heat flow province and is usually about 0.6 of the total heat flow, suggesting that in continental lithosphere, 60% of the heat comes from the lower crust or below and 40% is generated within the upper crust. We will now go on to investigate the distribution of radioactive heat generation in the crust.

There are two models for the distribution of radioactive heat generation consistent with the observation that there is a linear relationship between surface heat flow and heat generation (Figure 2.8 and Equation 2.1). The first model assumes that heat generation is distributed uniformly within the crust. The second model assumes that heat generation decreases exponentially with depth within the crust. The second model is more complex, but it is consistent with the observed linear relationship between surface heat flow and heat generation even in regions of differential erosion.

Neither of these models allows for the different distributions of the radioactive heat-producing isotopes. In other words, both models treat all the elements in the same way, although there is evidence that they are not distributed in the same way. For example, K may have fractionated from U or Th during igneous or sedimentary processes within the crust. Both models are consistent with the variations in measured surface heat flow, but the second model is likely to be closer to the real situation as most geochemical models for the crust predict that the concentration of radioactive isotopes decreases with depth.

To summarize, we have found that much of the variation in measured surface heat flow in continental regions is caused by radioactive heat generation in the crust. The reduced heat flow is the heat flow into the base of the crust. We will now consider how heat flow in continental lithosphere is related to its age.

2.5.1 Continental heat flow and age

As we saw in Section 2.4, there is a clear relationship between age and heat flow in oceanic lithosphere. Continental lithosphere is rather more complicated, and we have already seen that adjacent provinces have different thermal properties, so it would be reasonable to expect that any relationship between heat flow and age in continental lithosphere would not be simple. Table 2.6 and Figure 2.9 (overleaf) illustrate some of this complexity.

Table 2.6   Continental heat flow.

Age	Average heat flow (mW m^{-2})	No. of measurements
Subaqueous continental undifferentiated (lakes, continental shelf and slope)	77.7 ± 53.6	295
Cenozoic sedimentary and metamorphic	63.9 ± 27.5	2912
Cenozoic igneous	97.0 ± 66.9	3705
Mesozoic sedimentary and metamorphic	63.7 ± 28.2	1359
Mesozoic igneous	64.2 ± 28.8	1591
Paleozoic sedimentary and metamorphic	61.0 ± 30.2	403
Paleozoic igneous	57.7 ± 20.5	1810
Proterozoic	58.3 ± 23.6	260
Archean	51.5 ± 25.6	963

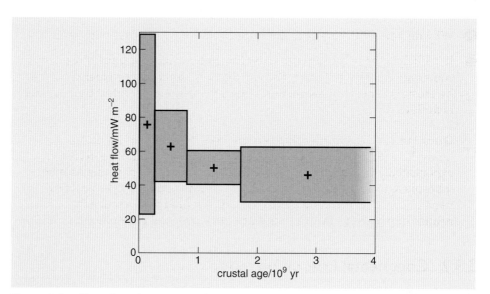

Figure 2.9   Heat flow data averaged into groups according to approximate radiometric crustal age for each site. Red boxes around the crosses (which represent average values) indicate uncertainties of the data.

● Can you see any relationship at all between heat flow and age from the data in Table 2.6?

● There is a lot of variability in the data, but as Figure 2.9 illustrates, there is a general trend towards increased heat flow in the younger lithosphere.

The age of continental lithosphere is much more difficult to quantify than for oceanic lithosphere because of the many cycles of heating, uplift and erosion that have affected any one crustal section. However, if reduced heat flow is plotted against age for a range of heat flow provinces, then any relationship that exists between heat flow and age should become apparent (see Figure 2.10).

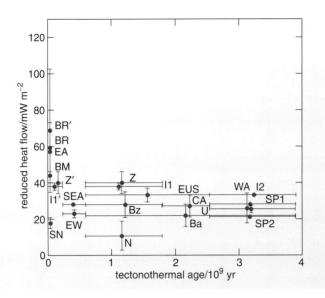

Figure 2.10 Reduced heat flow for a variety of heat flow provinces as a function of the time since the last thermal event (tectonothermal age). BR and BR′ Basin and Range; SEA SE Appalachians, USA; SN Sierra Nevada, USA; EUS Eastern USA; SP1 and SP2 Superior, USA; Bz Brazilian coastal shield; Ba Baltic shield; BM Bohemian massif; U Ukraine; EW England and Wales; N Niger; Z and Z′ Zambia; WA Western Australia; EA Eastern Australia; I1 and I1′ Indian shield; I2 Archean Indian shield; CA = Central Australia.

Although there is a fair amount of scatter in the data, there is a general trend towards decreasing heat flow from the deep crust and mantle with increasing age. Reduced heat flow appears to fall over the period 0–300 Ma and then to settle at a mean of about 25 mW m^{-2} for ages greater than 300 Ma.

● Why do you think continental reduced heat flow decreases with age?

● It is likely to be because continental lithosphere, like oceanic lithosphere, cools and thickens with age. Radioactive heat-producing elements are lost by erosion, especially in orogenic belts, but that will not affect the reduced heat flow.

Question 2.4 The relationship between heat flow and age for oceanic lithosphere (Figure 2.3a) can be described as follows. Heat flow decreases exponentially from values in excess of 250 mW m^{-2} for very young oceanic lithosphere to about 50 mW m^{-2} by 100 Ma. From 100 to 170 Ma, heat flow remains constant at around 50 mW m^{-2}. How would you describe the relationship between heat flow and age for continental lithosphere?

2.5.2 Continental heat of formation

Tectonic processes such as extension, hot-spot activity, crustal thickening and uplift cause transient heating of the continental lithosphere. An example for oceanic lithosphere comes from Hawaii, where the lithosphere is reheated by a hot spot. An example for continental lithosphere comes from the Snake River Plain, Wyoming, in the continental United States. This magmatic province results from intraplate volcanism that produced flood basalts and massive magmatic intrusions in the uppermost crust starting about 16 Ma ago and is thought to mark the passage of the North American Plate over the Yellowstone hot spot. Heat flow increases systematically eastwards towards the region of most recent volcanism from about 75–90 mW m^{-2} to 90–110 mW m^{-2}, well above the average for the surrounding areas. During extension or rifting of continental lithosphere, additional heat is added to the near surface by upward advection of heat from magmatic intrusions and crustal thinning. Simple models of the process of lithospheric extension, which produce a rifted continental margin or sedimentary basin, suggest that although heat is added to the crust, the additional heat flow will almost certainly dissipate rapidly in the first few hundred million years. It is not surprising therefore that heat flow for igneous, sedimentary and metamorphic regions is similar for the older regions of Mesozoic or Paleozoic ages (Table 2.6).

Within continental lithosphere, about 60% of the heat comes from lower crustal or mantle sources and the remaining 40% comes from heat-producing isotopes within the upper crust. Models for the distribution of these isotopes range from (i) a uniform vertical distribution, to (ii) one that decreases exponentially with depth. The second model seems more likely on the basis of geochemical evidence. Following on from the discussion above about variations with age of lithosphere, we can now recognize three components that contribute to our understanding of heat flow in continental lithosphere. These are:

1   The slowly decaying radiogenic contribution from the upper crust (area I of Figure 2.11).

2   The more rapidly decaying 'heat of formation' (area II on Figure 2.11).

3   The constant background rising from the lower crust and underlying mantle (area III on Figure 2.11).

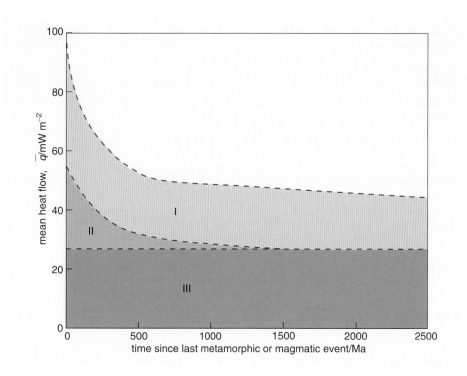

Figure 2.11   Decrease of mean continental heat flow with age and its three principal components. I is the radiogenic heat from the upper crust. II is heat from the metamorphic and magmatic events. III is the background heat from the lower crust and mantle. I decreases slowly from 0 to 2500 Ma, II decreases from 0 to 1500 Ma, and III is constant.

2.6   Global heat loss

Continental crust contains two to three times the abundance of radiogenic heat-producing isotopes and hence heat-producing capacity of oceanic crust. However, as Table 2.7 shows, the mean oceanic lithosphere heat flow is greater than that of continental lithosphere.

⬤   How do the mean heat flow values in Table 2.7 compare with the ranges of heat flow values for oceanic lithosphere (Figure 2.3) and continental lithosphere (Figure 2.10) you have already encountered?

● The ranges shown in Figures 2.3 and 2.9 are wide and cover the whole age spectrum for lithosphere. The average age of oceanic lithosphere is less than that of continental lithosphere, and for both types, the average age is less than half the maximum age. It is therefore impossible to derive mean heat flow values from these diagrams. From that point of view they can be misleading as the surface area that the data points represent is not shown.

Table 2.7 Mean heat flow values for oceanic and continental lithosphere.

Region	Mean heat flow (mW m^{-2})	No. of data
Oceanic	101 ± 2.2	9864
Continental	65 ± 1.6	10 337
Global	87 ± 2.0	20 201

Oceanic and continental heat flow account for about 70% and 30% respectively of the integrated surface heat flow.

The global average is 87 mW m^{-2}, which is equivalent to a total heat loss of 4.42 × 10^{13} W. It is rather more difficult to estimate the total heat production within the Earth, but the best estimate at present is 27.5 × 10^{12} W. Dividing the total heat production estimate by the global heat loss,

$$27.5 \times 10^{12} \, \text{W} / 4.42 \times 10^{13} \, \text{W} = 0.6.$$

This indicates that about 60% of the Earth's present heat output is from radioactive decay. The rest (40%) is residual heat loss from accretion and probably more importantly core formation. It is important to understand the distribution of heat sources in order to model the thermal evolution of the Earth satisfactorily.

2.6.1 Oceanic and continental geotherms

It is an interesting observation that the average heat flow in old oceanic lithosphere (>65 Ma) is the same as for the oldest continental lithosphere (>1000 Ma), that is about 50 mW m^{-2} (Figures 2.3 and 2.9, and Table 2.6). This may be a coincidence or it may be a fundamental consequence of plate tectonics. Oceanic geotherms are thought to be relatively simple and are described by conductive cooling in the plate model (Section 2.3). Temperature varies with depth along a straight geotherm to the base of the plate. The relationship (Figure 2.12) is described by the equation

$$q_s = k \, \frac{T}{z} \tag{2.2}$$

which can be rearranged to become

$$z = \frac{k}{q_s} \, T \tag{2.3}$$

where T is the temperature, z is depth, q_s is the surface heat flow, k is thermal conductivity and assuming $T = 0$ when $z = 0$. This is the equation of a straight line and it can be rearranged to show change in depth (Δz) against change in temperature (ΔT) thus

$$\Delta z = \frac{k}{q_s} \, \Delta T \tag{2.4}$$

Solving for temperature and removing the subscript on the heat flow, it becomes

$$\Delta T = \frac{q}{k}\,\Delta z \tag{2.5}$$

This is the form in which you will revisit the depth/temperature relationship in Block 4.

Below the base of the plate, temperature increases more slowly due only to the increasing pressure. This steady increase of temperature below the lithosphere with pressure (depth) is called the adiabatic gradient and it is about 0.3 °C km^{-1}. You will encounter the adiabatic gradient again in Block 4. In contrast, the continental geotherm depends on the variation of radioactive heat production with depth.

⬤   What two models are used to describe this variation?

⬤   (i) A uniform distribution of radioactive isotopes with depth and (ii) an exponentially decreasing concentration with depth.

Surface heat flow for old continental lithosphere is about the same as that for old oceanic lithosphere but the relationship illustrated in Figure 2.12 shows that at a given depth, old continental lithosphere is at a lower temperature than oceanic lithosphere. The curvature of the continental geotherm is characteristic of a layer with radioactive heat generation. The oceanic geotherm in contrast is linear because of a lack of heat generation. The change in slope for the oceanic geotherm occurs at the base of the lithosphere (shown here as 95 km) as the process of heat transfer changes from being predominantly convective (asthenosphere) to conductive (lithosphere). For the calculation of the continental geotherm shown in Figure 2.12, it was assumed that heat production was 2.5 × 10^{-6} W m^{-3} for the upper 8 km, an order of magnitude less for the lower crust and even less for the mantle. The resulting geotherm suggests that the thickness of old continental lithosphere exceeds that of old oceanic lithosphere.

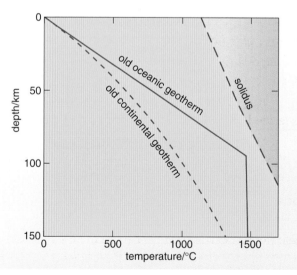

Figure 2.12 Geotherms for old oceanic (solid line) and old continental (short dashed line) lithosphere assuming a surface heat flow of 50 mW m^{-2}. The mantle solidus is shown as a long dashed line.

The geotherms come together below the base of the lithosphere, suggesting that there is not a significant thermal difference between mantle beneath old continental lithosphere and the mantle beneath old oceanic lithosphere. Bringing all this information together, the cartoon in Figure 2.13 summarizes our current understanding of old oceanic and old continental lithosphere thickness.

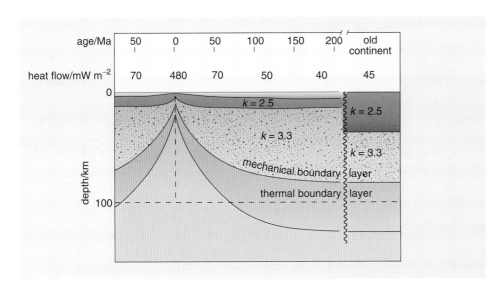

Figure 2.13 Thermal models for oceanic and old continental lithospheric plates. The dashed line represents the thickness predicted by the plate model. Recent estimates put this as low as 95 km, but the value of 125 km is also widely accepted. Thermal conductivity values (k) are in W m^{-1}°C^{-1} and heat flow is in mW m^{-2}.

2.7   Summary of Section 2

• Relatively little heat is generated within oceanic lithosphere.

• Oceanic lithosphere is fairly uniform in composition.

• Boundary layer and plate models can be used to predict the relationship of oceanic heat flow and depth with age.

• The Global Depth and Heat flow plate model fits the data best for lithosphere older than 65 Ma, probably because sealing at this age allows the lithosphere to lose heat mainly through conduction (which the model assumes).

• For ages younger than 65 Ma, all models overestimate heat flow in oceanic lithosphere, suggesting that heat flow in these regions is a result of convection as well as conduction.

• There is some relationship between surface heat flow and age in continental regions, with greater heat flow in younger lithosphere.

• Continental heat flow data indicate that there are regions with similar characteristics. These are called heat flow provinces.

• About 60% of the observed continental heat flow is from the lower crust and mantle. This is termed reduced heat flow and it is constant within a heat flow province.

• The remaining 40% of the observed continental surface heat flow is generated by radiogenic isotopes within the upper crust.

• Over the period 0 to about 1500 Ma, 'heat of formation' heat flow decreases with age since last metamorphic or magmatic heating event.

• Background heat flow from the lower crust and mantle is constant for each heat flow province and for older ages (Paleozoic and Precambrian) is everywhere about 25 mW m^{-2}.

• Old oceanic lithosphere and old continental lithosphere have about the same average surface heat flow.

• Heat flow is not uniformly distributed through the lithosphere. Radiogenic heat production falls off (probably exponentially) with depth in continental crust and it is much lower in oceanic lithosphere.

Objectives for Section 2

Now that you have completed this Section, you should be able to:

2.1   Understand the meaning of all the terms printed in **bold.**

2.2   Identify the sources of heat within the Earth.

2.3   Describe the variation of heat flow, depth and age for oceanic lithosphere.

2.4   Describe the main differences between the boundary layer and plate models.

2.5   Explain why the models do not fit the observations of heat flow and depth for all ages.

2.6   Describe the variation of heat flow, with age and province, for continental lithosphere.

2.7   Discuss the relationship between oceanic and continental lithospheric thickness and age.

Now try the following questions to test your understanding of Section 2.

Question 2.5   Explain briefly how the boundary layer and plate models for oceanic lithosphere differ. Which model fits the observed seismic and heat flow most satisfactorily?

Question 2.6   Explain how the depth of the boundary between the lithosphere and asthenosphere is defined.

Question 2.7   At a given depth, old continental lithosphere is at a lower temperature than oceanic lithosphere (Figure 2.12). Explain why this is the case in two to three sentences.

3 Strengths and weaknesses in the lithosphere

In the previous Section, you saw how heat flow measured at the surface of the Earth can be used to develop models for the thickness of the lithosphere. A surprising outcome is that old oceanic and continental lithosphere are similar in terms of heat flow. Oceanic lithosphere though tends to be covered with oceans and gets subducted beneath the continental lithosphere, whereas continents do not disappear. So there are clearly some significant differences between the two. In this Section, you will review the physical properties that determine the strength of the lithosphere. You will also discover that oceanic lithosphere is much stronger than continental lithosphere and that both are stronger in compression than extension. These features explain a great deal about the tectonics underpinning the topics of Blocks 2, 3 and 4.

3.1 The science of deformation

A fascinating area of materials science is the study of how and why materials deform the way they do. Why does custard flow better when it is hot than when it is cold? Why do shelves eventually bow under the weight of books? Materials deform (change shape) when a force is applied to them. If the material — and this can be a wooden shelf, a bowl of custard or a section of lithosphere — is able to go back to its original shape after the force has been removed, then it is said to have undergone **elastic deformation**. An everyday example is the stretching of an elastic band, so that when you stop pulling it and let go, the band reverts to its unstretched shape. However, if you keep pulling, eventually the elastic band breaks. It behaves elastically up to a certain threshold of applied force, after which it behaves in a non-elastic way, i.e. it snaps!

The force applied per unit area is a type of pressure called **stress** and is defined in Equation 3.1:

stress = force/area over which the force acts. (3.1)

The units of this stress are N m^{-2} or pascals (Pa).

Deformation (strain) is defined as:

strain = change in length/original length. (3.2)

For elastic deformation, strain is directly proportional to the stress. For stresses greater than a critical value, permanent deformation will occur, and this is illustrated in Figure 3.1.

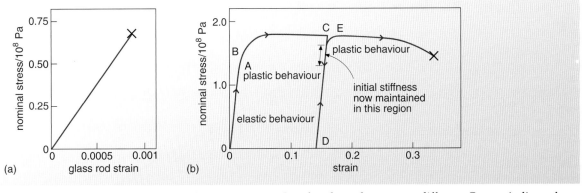

Figure 3.1 Stress–strain graphs for (a) a glass rod and (b) a copper wire. Note that the scales are very different. Crosses indicate the point at which the materials break. (a) For the glass rod, the relationship between stress and strain is linear and the rod deforms elastically up to the point at which it breaks. (b) The copper wire behaves elastically at first, up to A, and then it begins to behave plastically. The stress is still increasing to C, but this is not apparent from this graph because the wire is getting thinner and the stress plotted is nominal stress, which is force/original cross-sectional area. If the stress is removed and later reapplied, the wire will deform elastically along the line DE.

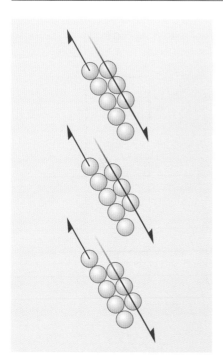

Figure 3.2 Cartoon of the molecular structure of copper. The force required to slide one layer of atoms over another may not be very great. Although the material does not break, it has deformed permanently.

The glass rod (Figure 3.1a) behaves elastically until it breaks. You cannot bend glass (unless you heat it, and we shall come onto this later). Over very long periods, glass may flow — windows in ancient buildings exemplify this, although the phenomenon of ancient glass being thicker at the bottom may also be due to impurities and the techniques of manufacture. So, time is an important factor in the response of a material to an applied stress. The copper wire (Figure 3.1b) behaves elastically at first, between 0 and A, and if the stress were removed at A, then the wire would return to its original length. Once it has passed B, the elastic strain recovers, but the wire is a little longer because of irreversible plastic strain. Even for small increases in stress after this critical point, there are very large increases in strain. This behaviour is termed **plastic deformation**. If the stress is removed at C, then the wire ends up with a permanent strain deformation (D). If the stress is again applied, the wire will stretch in the same way as it did before, along the line DE. The gradient of the line is a measure of the stiffness of the material and this is the same as before the original stress was applied. However, the critical stress has increased (E is a greater nominal stress than A, Figure 3.1b) and so the copper wire has actually become stronger and can sustain more elastic strain. This process of becoming stronger by the application of stress is called **strain hardening** and we shall return to it in the context of lithospheric deformation in Section 3.4.

So, why does the glass wire break and the copper wire eventually flow plastically? The answer lies in the molecular structure of the materials. Materials with an ordered structure (such as copper wire) have layers of molecules that can slide over each other (Figure 3.2). It is also because the copper atoms are bound by weak metallic bonds whereas in glass, the interatomic bonds are covalent and much stronger. A silicate mineral with a crystalline structure would behave in a similar way to the glass rod at room temperature.

Silicate minerals have a crystalline structure. Crystalline materials are full of imperfections and these can make the material behave differently from the way we would predict for a perfect material. An example of crystalline imperfection is a dislocation (Figure 3.3a). Dislocations allow a material to deform plastically at much lower stresses than would otherwise be possible.

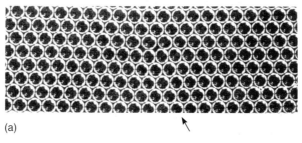

(a)

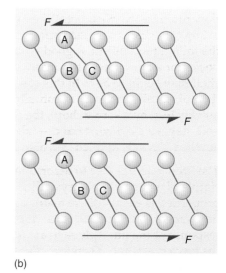

(b)

Figure 3.3 Dislocations in a crystalline material. (a) Photograph of a bubble model of crystalline material dislocation. You will find the dislocation most easily if you raise the page to eye level and look along the rows of bubbles following the arrow. (b) Cartoon showing how a dislocation moves when a stress F is applied. Atom A is pushed to the left, it forms a bond with B, and the bond with C weakens and breaks. The dislocation has moved to the right and can continue to do so until it reaches the edge of the material or another dislocation.

In contrast, the glass rod breaks by brittle fracture and does not yield like the copper wire. A tiny crack (but larger than an atom) within or on the surface of a material is the origin of brittle failure. Surprisingly perhaps, the smaller the crack, the more probable brittle failure becomes. For a large deep crack, the stress is accommodated more easily, but in a small crack, all the force acts on a small area (Figure 3.4). Thick glass can be cut cleanly by lightly scoring the surface and then simply tapping the glass. If a deeper and blunter scratch is made, the glass will not cut cleanly and may not break in the right place at all.

● Are crystalline materials susceptible to failure at cracks?

● When a crack occurs in a crystalline material, the material yields and the stress is accommodated over a large area and is not concentrated in one spot. This facility to yield is a property of **ductile** behaviour and reflects an ability to flow. Once a critical limit is reached however, the material will break.

Table 3.1 summarizes the differences between brittle and ductile behaviour.

Table 3.1 Failure mechanisms in glasses and crystalline materials.

	Glasses	Crystalline materials
Brittle fracture?	Yes, when cold	Yes, when cold, no when warm because flow at the tip of the crack relieves the stress concentration. Fracture will occur eventually after the plastic limit has been exceeded
Ductile yielding?	No, because there are no planes of molecules which could slip over each other	Yes

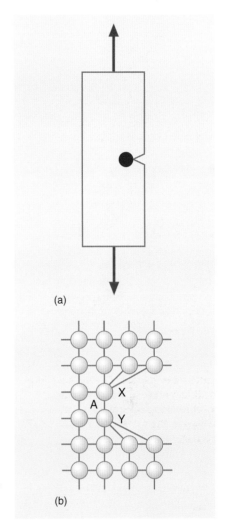

(a)

(b)

Figure 3.4 The effect of a small crack in a glass. (a) Stress is greatest in the coloured circular area behind the crack. (b) Force at A is large as it needs to balance the forces on the atoms at X and Y from above and below. The diagram is highly schematic, because glass has an irregular structure, not neat rows of atoms.

What does this have to do with a bowl of custard or wooden bookshelf, and how does all this relate to the lithosphere? Well, depending on how thick your custard is, it should flow rather than crack and so some of its properties are similar to those of the crystalline materials described above. It is also able to flow more easily when hot. When it cools, the viscosity increases to such an extent that cracking at the surface can occur. Thus, temperature will influence the failure mechanism. A good wooden bookshelf can withstand the force due to books for a long time. After many years of holding up great tomes though, the shelf may begin to bow. In this case, the shelf would be deforming elastically, then plastically and may eventually undergo brittle fracture. If a force is applied quickly (e.g. by a karate chop), the shelf may fracture immediately. (Alternatively, you may have a broken hand — also as a result of brittle fracture!) Thus, the rate at which stress is applied will also influence the failure mechanism.

The lithosphere is able to deform in all these ways too. Its structure is not like a simple glass or a simple crystalline solid (Table 3.1), but it has some of the same properties as each of these materials. Like the custard, the response of the lithosphere to an applied force depends on temperature. Like the bookshelf, the response of the lithosphere to an applied force depends on the time over which the force is applied. Therefore, the strain rate is an important property to measure when considering lithospheric deformation and is defined (using Equation 3.2) in Equation 3.3. We shall return to this concept in a moment.

$$\text{strain rate} = \frac{\text{strain}}{\text{time}} = \frac{\text{change in length (m)}}{\text{original length (m)} \times \text{time (s)}} \quad (3.3)$$

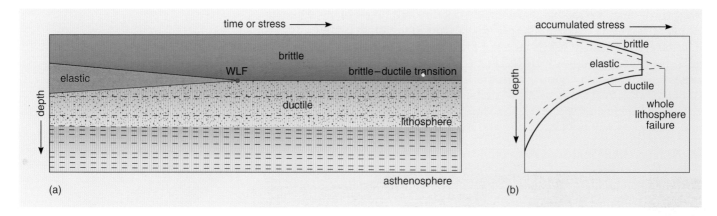

(a)

(b)

Figure 3.5 (a) The relationship between brittle, elastic and ductile behaviour in the lithosphere with increasing stress and/or time. The most shallow (cold) region is always brittle. For small stresses, the lithosphere deforms mostly elastically, but there comes a point at which it is no longer able to accommodate the stress in this way and it fails. As the lower part is hotter and able to flow in a ductile manner, it does not deform elastically. When elastic deformation can no longer occur, the whole lithosphere deforms permanently in a process called whole lithosphere failure (WLF). (b) Relationship between the accumulation of stress in the elastic layer shown in Figure 3.5a and depth. The layer above is yielding by brittle deformation and the region below is deforming by ductile flow. As time and/or stress magnitude increase, the regions of brittle and ductile failure coalesce (dashed line) and the initially elastic layer begins to fail. Once it has failed, the accumulated stress dissipates rapidly (bottom part of dashed line).

The unit of strain rate is s^{-1}. These relationships are illustrated in the cartoon in Figure 3.5.

The response of the lithosphere to an applied stress depends on one or more of the following: (i) the amount of time over which a stress is applied; (ii) the magnitude of the stress; and (iii) temperature. Near the surface, where rocks are cold, the deformation is brittle. Rocks deform elastically at first and then cracks open up and brittle failure follows. Volcanoes can undergo several metres of elastic deformation (Figure 3.6) over a period of months or years, but fractures open up when the stress becomes too great (Figure 3.7).

Figure 3.6 The Campi Flegrei volcanic caldera near Naples, Italy, has undergone vertical movement resulting from several cycles of elastic uplift and deflation. During a crisis in the 1980s, the central part of the caldera at Serapeo was uplifted by 1.8 m over a period of just two years possibly due to the intrusion of fresh magma into the underlying magma chamber.

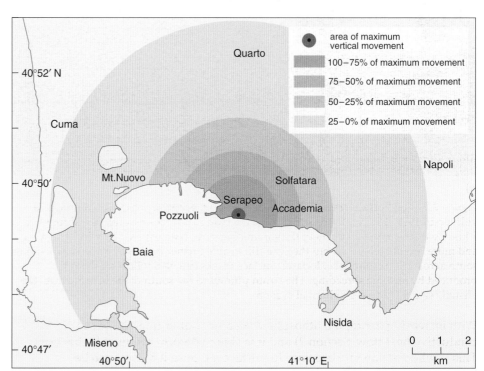

(a)

(b)

Figure 3.7 (a) Surface cracks which formed during eruptive activity at Mount Etna volcano in 1989. The cracks trend SSE from the summit crater area and extend for over 7 km. Evidence of the cracks near the summit has now been covered by windblown ash and more recent lava flows, but they are still visible further downslope. (b) View looking south across Thingvellir lake, Iceland. Surface cracks run N–S following the rift produced by tectonic spreading. The steam plumes to the south of the lake are from the Hengil central volcano geothermal system.

With increasing depth, the lithosphere becomes hotter (mainly due to conductive heat flow, Section 2) and it is able to deform through ductile flow. This is where strain rate becomes important, because if a stress can be accommodated through deformation at least as fast as the stress is applied, then there will be no stress accumulation. The implications of stress accumulation in earthquake zones and regions of faulting are discussed in Block 4 Section 2.5.

Question 3.1 For a strain rate of $10^{-15}\,\text{s}^{-1}$, by how much would a 1 m length of a material deform in 10 Ma? (Assume that there are $3.15 \times 10^7\,\text{s}$ in a year.)

Thus, in this example, just over 0.3 m of expansion (or contraction) will occur per metre. If the deformation happens over 10 Ma, there will be no accumulated stress.

Question 3.2 Assuming typical spreading and subduction rates of the order of $1–3\,\text{cm yr}^{-1}$ (Section 1), what will be the strain rate along a 1000-km-wide lithospheric plate?

Consequently, the slowest geologically significant strain rates (in terms of plate-scale tectonics) are of the order of $10^{-16}\,\text{s}^{-1}$. Although many of the physical properties of rocks and minerals are still uncertain, especially at the pressures and temperatures found deep within the Earth, the strain rates of some geologically interesting materials have been measured experimentally. The stress applied in the experiments summarized in Figure 3.8 is $50 \times 10^6\,\text{Pa}$ (i.e. 50 MPa).

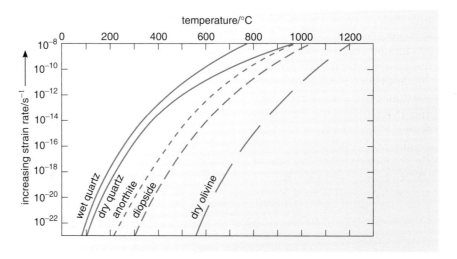

Figure 3.8 Variation of strain rate with temperature at a constant extensional stress of 50 MPa for some geologically significant materials. Ductile behaviour will only occur on the high temperature side of each curve for a particular material.

Question 3.3 Assuming an extensional stress of 50 MPa, at what temperatures do quartz (wet and dry), plagioclase feldspar, pyroxene and olivine reach a geologically significant strain rate?

The upper continental crust may be considered to comprise varying amounts of quartz and feldspar, and the upper mantle to comprise largely olivine, but what about the lower crust? We have less reliable information about this region, but it is thought to comprise mafic granulite, which is a metamorphic rock containing Ca-feldspar and Mg-pyroxene. From Figure 3.8, it would appear that the lower crust would begin to deform at 450 °C. For a geotherm corresponding to a heat flow of $50\,\text{mW m}^{-2}$ (Figure 2.12), this temperature would be encountered at a depth of about 40 km. So, assuming that anorthite is present in the lower crust, it seems highly likely that much of the lower crust will deform in a ductile manner. Only the upper crust will behave in an elastic fashion.

Question 3.4 Using the geotherm in Figure 2.12 and the information in Figure 3.8, at what depths would you expect ductile deformation to occur in the upper continental crust and the upper continental mantle for a strain rate of $10^{-16}\,\text{s}^{-1}$? Discuss your results in three to four sentences.

So to summarize, the upper mantle and much of the lower crust is likely to be ductile. At depths in excess of 10–15 km, the upper crust may also be ductile; however, at shallow depths, it is elastic and fails eventually by brittle fracture. The way in which a material responds to applied stress depends on temperature and the duration of the stress and on the composition of the material being stressed. **Rheology** is the study of these material properties.

3.2 Failure of the lithosphere — under extension

Using the division of the continental lithosphere made above into a quartz-rich upper crust, a plagioclase-rich lower crust and an olivine-rich upper mantle, models have been developed to investigate variations in lithosphere rheology. One model (Figure 3.9) assumes average heat flow of 60 mW m^{-2} for continental lithosphere and a constant extensional stress of 10 MPa over a period of 1 Ma. Notice that this is a rather lower stress than we considered above. After 1000 years, according to this model, below about 45 km, the upper mantle has deformed by ductile flow and has no stress accumulated in it. Thus, the stress is concentrated in the layers above and so the accumulated stress at these higher levels is greater than the average stress applied. The actual depth (45 km in this model) depends on heat flow and the corresponding geotherm, but it is between the values deduced in Question 3.4. After 1000 years, no permanent deformation above 45 km has occurred. Over the next 100 000 years (Figure 3.9), the stress continues to increase and at the bases of the lower crust and upper crust (35 km and 18 km in this model) the limit of elastic behaviour is reached. At these points, ductile behaviour begins. If you look back at Figure 2.12, although the geotherm is slightly different from the one assumed here, it is still clear that at about 45 km depth, continental lower crust will be at a temperature of about 500 °C. From Figure 3.8, it is clear that the lower crust is ductile at this point (for a strain rate of 10^{-16} s^{-1}).

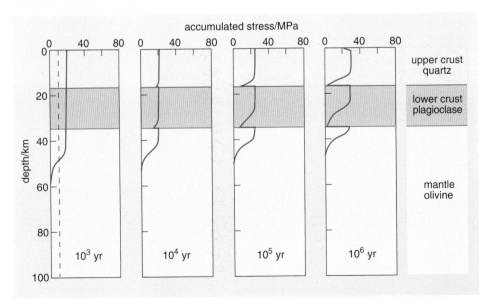

Figure 3.9 Comparison of accumulated stress and depth through time for a model of 100-km-thick lithosphere with an applied stress of 10 MPa over 1 Ma.

● What about the upper crust?

◑ From Figures 2.12, 3.8 and 3.9, at about 18 km, the temperature is about 300 °C and quartz is beginning to become ductile.

However, the material above about 18 km does not behave in a ductile manner, because it is too cold (Figures 2.12 and 3.8). Thus, stress will continue to accumulate in the upper parts of these layers while the lower parts begin to alleviate the stress by ductile flowing. This is the process of **stress amplification**. The applied stress is being increasingly accommodated within a thinning region, below which ductile flow inhibits stress accumulation.

● What would happen if the stress were to be applied for a few more million years?

◐ It is clear from Figure 3.9 that the elastic region in each of the layers is becoming thinner with time. Initially (after 1000 years), the whole of the upper and lower crust and the top 10 km of the upper mantle were behaving elastically. After 1 Ma, only the top 1–12 km or so of the upper crust and the top 5 km of the lower crust are still elastic. After a few more million years, these elastic regions will shrink further.

● What is the significance of the nick in the curve at the top of the upper crust that appears after 1 Ma (Figure 3.9)?

◑ Accumulated stress below the first few kilometres has increased because the region above has failed. It is no longer behaving elastically and has undergone brittle failure with fractures appearing at the surface.

At some time after about 1 Ma, this model predicts that the ductile region migrates up to join the brittle fracture region (Figure 3.5b) and the whole lithosphere fails. After this occurs, the stress has been alleviated and the process will start again if a new stress is applied.

These results are highly model-dependent, as Figure 3.10 illustrates. All other things being equal (the same lithospheric model and applied stress for 1 Ma have been used), for a much lower heat flow of 45 mW m^{-2}, stress is accumulated to a depth of 70 km, well down into the mantle before ductile flow begins. At the other extreme, for a heat flow of 90 mW m^{-2}, there is a huge stress accumulation within the top few km, but ductile flow occurs within much of the upper crust, the lower half of the lower crust and within the upper mantle.

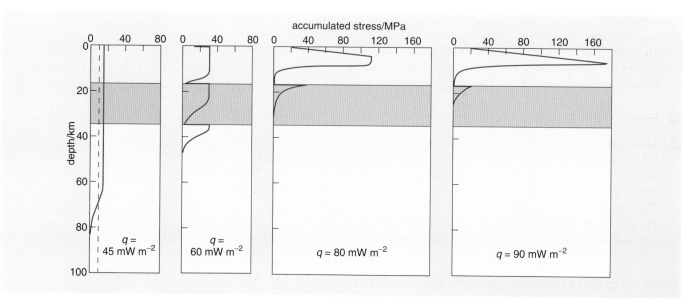

Figure 3.10 The effects of a range of heat flow values for the lithospheric model in Figure 3.9. The applied stress is 10 MPa over a 100-km-thick lithosphere for 1 Ma.

This brings us back to the bowl of custard. If a cooled bowl of custard is knocked, it may form some cracks in the top surface. Unless you have a very strange recipe and some peculiar conditions, the cracks will not penetrate to the bottom of the bowl. The lower parts of the custard will undergo ductile deformation and only the upper part is brittle. The same is true of the lithosphere. The upper part of the upper crust is subject to enormous stress because the lower regions dissipate stress (since they are hotter and ductile) and the remaining stress is amplified near the surface. Thus, the upper crust is subject to brittle failure, but the fractures do not penetrate very far. The stress at depth is alleviated by ductile flow, which is possible because of the higher temperatures at depth.

- What is the difference between the force applied to the bowl of custard in this thought experiment and the force applied to the lithosphere in the model described above?

- The force applied to the bowl of custard was a short, sharp shock, whereas the force applied to the lithospheric model is uniform over a period of 1 Ma.

The magnitude and duration of an applied stress determine the response of a material. When a heavy load (large stress) is applied for a long time, a wooden bookshelf behaves elastically, then plastically and may then undergo brittle failure, but for a very short-duration stress (e.g. the karate chop experiment), it can become brittle very rapidly. Another everyday example is children's 'potty putty', which behaves elastically when bounced on the floor and plastically when left on a flat surface. Similarly, the lithosphere and mantle are elastic for small or short-lived stresses such as earthquakes. If the mantle always deformed by ductile flow, then seismic S-waves would not be transmitted. For stresses applied over longer periods, even much of the strong upper crust will become ductile.

- Which of the three-layer models assumed in Figure 3.10 is strongest and how does it relate to the age of the lithosphere?

- From Figure 3.10, for the highest heat flow, much of the lithosphere is ductile. The accumulated stress in the upper part of the upper crust is very large, but eventually it undergoes brittle fracture. For lower heat flow, the whole of the crust and much of the upper mantle are elastic and therefore stronger. From Figure 2.9, you should remember that heat flow is generally higher in younger lithosphere and so the conclusion is that older lithosphere is stronger than younger lithosphere.

- How does the timing of whole lithosphere failure relate to lithosphere age?

- From Figure 3.10, after 1 Ma in the highest heat flow scenarios, almost the whole lithosphere has failed. There is just a small amount of accumulated stress still in the lower crust. The surface has fractured and there is a large stress in the upper part of the upper crust, but the rest has become ductile. The lowest heat flow model is not close to whole lithosphere failure, because most of the lithosphere is still elastic. Therefore, for a given applied stress, younger (higher heat flow) lithosphere will fail sooner than older lithosphere.

The stress needed to produce whole lithosphere failure in 1 Ma is called the **critical stress**. The models above were for an extensional stress, and similar models can be calculated for compressional stress. This is important because rocks have rather different properties under compression than under extension, as Figure 3.11 illustrates.

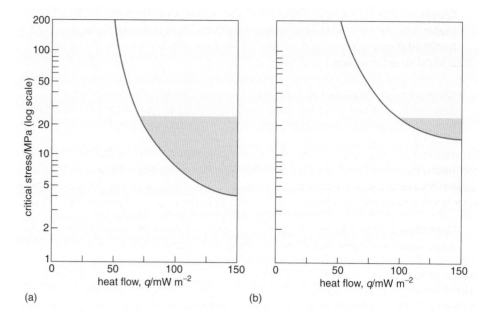

Figure 3.11 Critical stress needed to produce whole lithosphere failure in 1 Ma using the three-layer continental lithosphere model in Figure 3.9. The value of critical stress varies with heat flow, which is related to age of the lithosphere. Critical stress is lower for (a) extensional than for (b) compressional regimes. Notice that the vertical scale is logarithmic. The shaded region is discussed in the text.

For a critical stress of 50 MPa, the heat flow would need to be about $60\,\mathrm{mW\,m^{-2}}$ in an extensional regime but it would need to be about $75\,\mathrm{mW\,m^{-2}}$ in a compressional regime. In order to test whether these models are realistic, some real data are needed. One method of measuring elastic strain in the upper crust is to use strain gauges (Figure 3.12).

For the lower lithosphere, the stress must be inferred by estimating the masses involved and the strain rates from seismic data. The approximate values of the major tectonic stresses are summarized in Table 3.2 while the symbols and terminology used are defined in Section 1.3 and Figure 1.8.

Table 3.2 Comparison of the magnitude and nature of major tectonic stresses.

Mechanism	Symbol	Nature	Range of magnitude of stress, MPa
Subduction slab–pull	F_{SP}	extensional	0–50
Subduction trench suction	F_{SU}	extensional	0–30
Ridge–slide	F_{RS}	compressional	20–30
Mantle convective drag	R_{OD}, R_{CD}	both	1–10
Plateau uplift (like F_{RS} but on continental lithosphere)	F_{PU}	both, mainly extensional	50 (max.)

Figure 3.12 A photograph of a strain gauge measuring deformation across a crack on the Tebay section of the A6 road in the north of England.

The major tectonic forces acting on oceanic lithosphere are F_{SP} and F_{RS}. Added together, they could be as much as 80 MPa, but this is the force moving the lithosphere relative to the asthenosphere: it is not the force causing deformation within the lithosphere itself. Such a force would come from these tectonic forces acting in opposition, putting a stress on the lithosphere. An analogy for this comes from the bowl of custard, if the bowl were made of soft plastic or cardboard (think of a party!). The custard will not deform if it is carried in the bowl on a tray. It could travel quite fast, requiring a large force, but there is no deformation (unless you fall over). If the bowl is deformed though, either squashed or stretched, then the custard will deform because of the opposing stresses applied to it.

Question 3.5 Mark onto Figure 3.11 the maximum stress for each of the major tectonic forces using information from Table 3.2. You should draw a horizontal line extending from the stress axis past the line marking the critical stress and label each line.

Question 3.6 What is the theoretical maximum stress on continental lithosphere for tension and compression, and what heat flow is required for the critical stress to be attained under each of these regimes?

In Question 3.6, you deduced that the largest extensional stress acting on continental lithosphere ($F_{SU} + F_{PU}$) is about 80 MPa. However, the chance of both these forces acting to their maximum value in the same direction at the same time is very small and so we shall take a value of 25 MPa as a more reasonable maximum.

Question 3.7 For a critical stress of 25 MPa during extension, what is the minimum necessary heat flow for whole lithosphere failure to occur?

So, according to these models, through the processes of stress amplification, whole lithosphere failure will occur in an extensional regime for heat flows in excess of 70 mW m^{-2}. Some extension may occur for lower heat flows, especially if the stress is applied for longer periods, but the stronger lithosphere will make this more unlikely. How does the model compare with reality? Heat flow is measurable at the surface as you saw in Section 2 and it is clear at the surface when whole lithosphere failure has occurred, as for instance in the separation of Africa from South America or in the East African Rift (Block 2). Thus, comparing the estimated critical heat flow value of 70 mW m^{-2} with some real examples should provide an indication as to the validity of the model. Figure 3.13 illustrates results from various parts of the world.

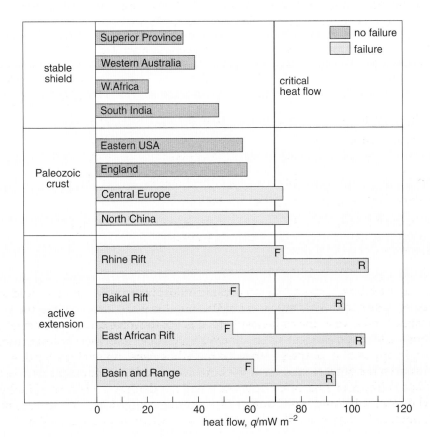

Figure 3.13 Mean heat flow for various parts of the world grouped into stable shields, regions that underwent tectonic activity in the Paleozoic and regions currently undergoing extension. For the currently active regions, heat flow values for both the rifts themselves (R) and the flank region (F) are given. In each case, the heat flow in the actively rifting regions is in excess of 70 mW m^{-2} as predicted by the models.

● Locate the actively extending regions of Figure 3.13 on *This Dynamic Planet* (DP).

● The Rhine Rift is a depression traversing part of northern Europe. The Baikal Rift is centred on the 1.5-km-deep Lake Baikal which marks the separation between the Siberian craton to the NW and several smaller plates to the SE. The East African Rift runs N–S through Ethiopia, Kenya and Tanzania. The Basin and Range Province again runs roughly N–S through the south-western USA.

The stable shield regions all have low heat flow and are not failing — indeed, they cannot fail. Looking back to Figure 3.11, it is clear that for heat flow of about $40 \, \text{mW m}^{-2}$, whole lithosphere failure would not occur until the stress was well in excess of $200 \, \text{MPa}$. From Table 3.2, it is also clear that this is impossible to achieve. The Paleozoic crust of the eastern USA and England have heat flow values ($\sim 60 \, \text{mW m}^{-2}$) that are lower than those for which an extensional stress of $25 \, \text{MPa}$ would become critical. Again, from Figure 3.11, a heat flow of $60 \, \text{mW m}^{-2}$ would imply a critical stress of about $65 \, \text{MPa}$ for lithospheric failure. This value is theoretically attainable, but is obviously not present in these regions at this time. In contrast, the higher heat flow experienced in Central Europe and North China ($75 \, \text{mW m}^{-2}$) requires a critical stress of only $20 \, \text{MPa}$. Both Central Europe and North China (see DP) are undergoing extensional failure and this should give you some confidence in the model. In the regions of current active extension, the heat flow at the rifting part is well in excess of that required by the model for whole lithosphere failure (Figures 3.11 and 3.13). The East African Rift is discussed in detail in Block 2.

3.3   Failure of the lithosphere — under compression

The major tectonic forces responsible for compression (note F_{SP} is extensional) in the lithosphere are F_{PU} and F_{RS} (Section 1.3, Figure 1.8 and Table 3.2). The highest plausible combined values for these is about $80 \, \text{MPa}$ (Table 3.2), but as for extension, a more reasonable value is about $25 \, \text{MPa}$.

Question 3.8 What is the minimum heat flow required for whole lithosphere failure during compression, given a critical stress of $25 \, \text{MPa}$? What does this value of heat flow imply about compression within a lithospheric plate?

It should now be clear that lithosphere is stronger in compression than in extension. But what about the Alps and the Himalaya — are they not regions of compressional deformation? They are certainly part of major continental lithosphere plates now, but both regions mark the suture joining separate plates. The deformation has occurred at the plate boundaries and not within the plates themselves.

● Would you expect to find the greatest stresses at the edges of tectonic plates or at the centre?

● The difference between the various stresses will be greatest at the boundaries between plates. Thus, the greatest stresses will be found at the edges of plates.

● What are the implications for compressional tectonic processes?

● It is most likely that they will occur at the boundaries of plates. This is indeed what is observed — volcanic, earthquake and major deformation events are located at the edges of plates.

So the lithospheric response to compressive stress is mainly localized at the boundaries of the plates. But which type of lithosphere is strongest? Looking back to Figure 3.8, you should be able to see that under extension, olivine and feldspar reach the geologically significant strain rate of $10^{-16}\,\mathrm{s}^{-1}$ at temperatures of about 750 °C and 450 °C. In contrast, quartz reaches this strain rate at temperatures of about 250 °C. This means that continental lithosphere, which is dominated in its upper region by quartz, will deform at much lower temperatures than oceanic lithosphere, which is dominated by plagioclase in the upper part and olivine below about 10 km. Thus, oceanic lithosphere is much stronger than continental lithosphere given the same conditions. Looking back to Figure 2.6, for a typical oceanic geotherm, the temperature at which olivine will begin to become ductile (750 °C) will not be reached until a depth in excess of 50 km. Above this depth, the lithosphere will behave elastically. A huge amount of stress amplification would be required to reach the critical stress.

- How would the heat flow/critical stress relationship for oceanic lithosphere compare with the relationship shown in Figure 3.11?

- Oceanic lithosphere is much stronger than continental lithosphere and higher heat flow would be needed in order to reach the critical stresses. Thus, the curves would plot further up and to the right of the curves in Figure 3.11.

For plausible stresses of say 25 MPa, unreasonably large heat flow would be needed (far in excess of $100\,\mathrm{mW\,m^{-2}}$) for oceanic lithosphere to become ductile. It is for this reason that deformation is rarely seen within oceanic lithosphere. At ocean ridges where the heat flow is highest, the stresses are also greatest. However, even here at the plate boundary, the ridge forms through thermal expansion and sinks elastically with age and distance from the boundary. The zero free-air gravity anomaly across most ridges (Figure 3.14) implies isostatic equilibrium, and this is consistent with a model in which hot, buoyant, low-density material underlies the ridge. Asthenospheric mantle is 'sucked into' the void created by the separating plates. A mass excess (positive free-air anomaly) would be expected if the ridge were underlain by 'extra' material of the same density emplaced by ductile flow.

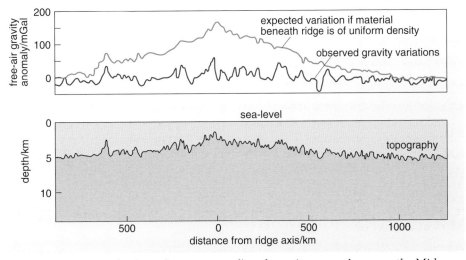

Figure 3.14 Topography (greatly exaggerated) and gravity anomaly across the Mid-Atlantic Ridge. The observed free-air gravity anomaly is essentially zero. There is therefore no excess mass and the region is in isostatic equilibrium. If the material beneath the ridge were all of the same density, the anomaly would have the form shown on the upper plot. The density of the material beneath the ridge must actually be lower than that of the surrounding material in order for the gravity values to be more or less constant as observed.

In summary, lithosphere is stronger in compression than it is in extension and oceanic lithosphere is much stronger than continental lithosphere. Younger lithosphere, characterized by higher heat flow is less strong than older lithosphere (with lower heat flow).

● Heat flow during the Archean was greater than it is now, resulting in steeper geotherms than at present. Would you expect lithosphere in the Archean to be stronger or weaker than more recent lithosphere?

● From Figures 3.8 and 3.11, it is clear that higher temperatures and heat flow will tend to favour ductile flow. Archean lithosphere would have been weaker than more recent lithosphere.

3.4   Why do plates fail?

The critical stress needed for whole lithosphere failure to occur depends on the relative proportions of quartz, feldspar and olivine in the lithosphere because these minerals determine its strength. Referring back to the 100 km model for continental lithosphere with crust to 35 km (Figure 3.9), we shall now consider what happens under extension and compression.

When the net applied force is extensional, the lithosphere is stretched, so that it becomes thinner. Unlike the copper wire, which deformed in isolation (Section 3.1), the lithosphere is connected to the asthenosphere, so when the lithosphere thins, the asthenosphere rises up to take its place (Figure 3.15).

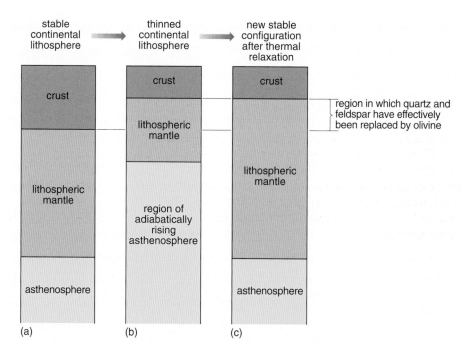

Figure 3.15 Continental lithosphere under extension. As the lithosphere thins, the asthenosphere rises up to take its place. After a new equilibrium has become established, the crust is thinner and the upper mantle is thicker than before.

● Can you remember what happened to the copper wire when it was extended?

● Once extension went beyond the critical point, the wire was permanently extended (Figure 3.1b). After relaxation, the process of strain hardening strengthened the wire so that it was able to withstand a greater extension before yielding if an extensional force was applied again.

Strain hardening also happens in the lithosphere and, from Figure 3.15, the source of the strength should be clear. The stretched and thinned lithosphere contains more olivine and less quartz and feldspar than the unstretched lithosphere. From Figure 3.8, olivine is clearly stronger than either quartz or feldspar at a given depth. The effect on the geotherm is illustrated in Figure 3.16. Three geotherms are shown: (i) the adjacent unstretched lithosphere, (ii) the transient geotherm during stretching and (iii) the final geotherm.

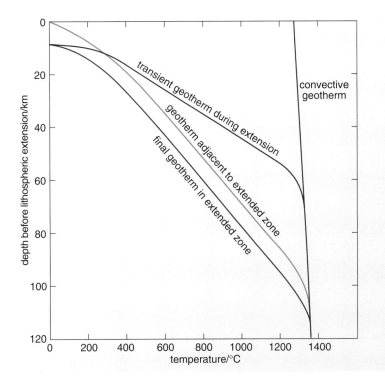

Figure 3.16 For the extension shown in Figure 3.15, the geothermal gradient initially steepens (the rate of change of temperature with depth increases) and then flattens out during thermal relaxation. It may help you to see the gradient steepening (transient) and then flattening (final steady state) if you turn the page around so that depth goes across the bottom of the Figure. Note the 8 km depth for 0 °C during extension indicates subsidence at the surface.

The Moho, which is a seismically defined discontinuity between the continental crust and upper mantle, is at 35 km depth in this model. Before extension, this boundary is at about 600 °C. Initially, the isotherms move upwards and the 600 °C isotherm rises to less than 30 km depth, creating a transient geotherm. As the stretched lithosphere cools and equilibrates towards a steady state in a process called **thermal relaxation**, the geotherm becomes more similar to the geotherm of adjacent, undeformed lithosphere, and the 600 °C isotherm is located below 40 km. Thus, after stretching, the lithosphere is cooler for a given depth than before.

> **Question 3.9** For the model used here, the base of the lithosphere is at a temperature of about 1340 °C at 100 km depth before stretching. Use Figures 3.15 and 3.16 to describe what happens to the base of the lithosphere during stretching.

Thus, during stretching, the lithosphere becomes less strong, but once the stress is removed, the process of strain hardening actually strengthens the lithosphere. The degree to which the strength of the lithosphere increases or decreases will depend on the length of time for which the stress is applied and the magnitude of the stress. If strain rate is high, the lithosphere will not be in equilibrium and thermal relaxation will not be able to keep up with extension. If this happens, the lithosphere is weakened. This process is called strain softening and you will encounter it again in Block 4. Strain softening, whereby strain continues to increase even if the stress is reduced, may result in rifting. This is simply the logical conclusion of the situation shown in Figures 3.15 and 3.16. If the stress applied (extension) is great enough, the asthenosphere may rise to the surface.

In contrast, for the slowest geologically significant strain rate of $10^{-16}\,\mathrm{s}^{-1}$, there is no transient geotherm and the base of the lithosphere moves down fast enough to keep pace with the thinning caused by extension. In this case, the 600 °C isotherm moves down from the Moho well into the upper mantle. The effect is to strengthen the lithosphere and is similar to ageing in that, for a given depth, temperature is lower and so the possibility of ductile flow is more remote.

Of course, there must be a limit to the increasing strength that lithosphere can acquire. Once strength becomes great enough, the lithosphere will be able to withstand further stress and so no more extension will occur and no more strengthening will occur either. The **lithospheric extension factor** β is the ratio of the initial to final lithosphere thickness. For a section of lithosphere of thickness a thinned by extension to a final thickness $0.67a$, the extension factor β = 1.5. Due to strain hardening, it turns out that for the strain rates we are considering ($10^{-16}\,\mathrm{s}^{-1}$), an applied stress of say 45 MPa must more than double for β to exceed 1.5. For higher strain rates of $10^{-14}\,\mathrm{s}^{-1}$ to $10^{-13}\,\mathrm{s}^{-1}$ however, if the initial stress is 75–90 MPa, then strain softening (the process by which lithosphere strength decreases during extension) means that a lower stress is needed to continue extension well beyond a β factor of 1.5. The difference between a strain rate of $10^{-15}\,\mathrm{s}^{-1}$ and $10^{-14}\,\mathrm{s}^{-1}$ marks the difference between strain hardening and strain softening.

> **Question 3.10** What is the time taken for a β factor of 1.5 to occur for these strain rates of $10^{-15}\,\mathrm{s}^{-1}$ and $10^{-14}\,\mathrm{s}^{-1}$?

This means that if it takes less than 1.6 Ma to achieve a β factor of 1.5, then strain softening will be the dominant process and, with decreasing lithospheric strength, the extension will continue. If it takes more than 16 Ma, then strain hardening will limit the extension to a β factor of 1.5, which is equivalent to 50% extension. These figures are highly model-dependent and so, in general, it is reasonable to round these figures to 1 Ma for strain softening and 10 Ma for strain hardening. These results are summarized on Figure 3.17.

For a compressional stress, the analysis is similar to the discussion above for extension. During compression at high strain rates, the crust and mantle will both thicken, increasing the overall thickness of the lithosphere (Figure 3.18). At high strain rates, the transient geotherm applies (Figure 3.19). The Moho, which is at 35 km and 600 °C, gets deeper and hotter initially and the lithosphere as a whole thickens. As the geothermal gradient becomes less steep (remember you

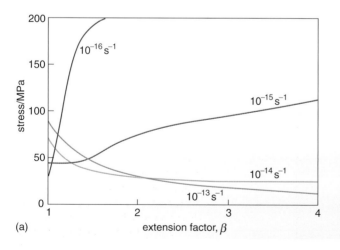

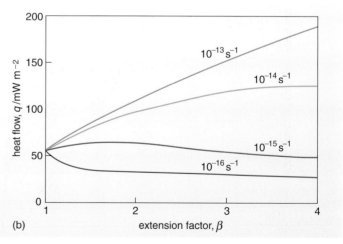

Figure 3.17 Lithosphere strength is defined here as the force required to maintain a given strain rate. For the lower strain rates of 10^{-15} and $10^{-16}\,\mathrm{s}^{-1}$, as the lithospheric stretch factor β increases, the strength increases (a) and the heat flow decreases (b) due to strain hardening. For the higher strain rates of $10^{-14}\,\mathrm{s}^{-1}$ and $10^{-13}\,\mathrm{s}^{-1}$, the strength decreases with increasing β (a) and heat flow increases (b) due to strain softening.

need to turn Figure 3.19 on its side to see this gradient become less steep), the lithosphere cools, so that for a given depth it is cooler than it was before compression. The lithosphere is therefore stronger than before compression, since colder lithosphere is stronger than hotter lithosphere. Thus, strain

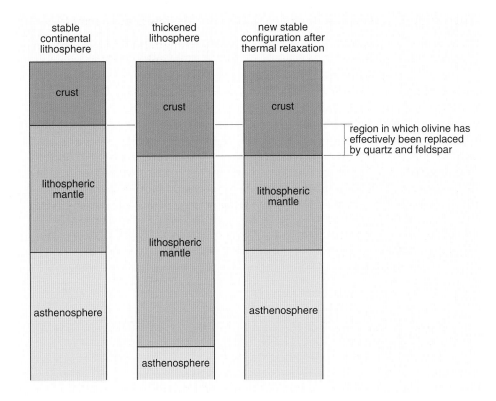

Figure 3.18 Stages in the evolution of a continental lithosphere profile undergoing compression. From the initial configuration, thickening at high strain rates allows no time for thermal equilibration. After thermal relaxation has occurred, the lithosphere has the same overall thickness as before, but has a larger (low-density) crustal component. This situation would be associated with a topographic high.

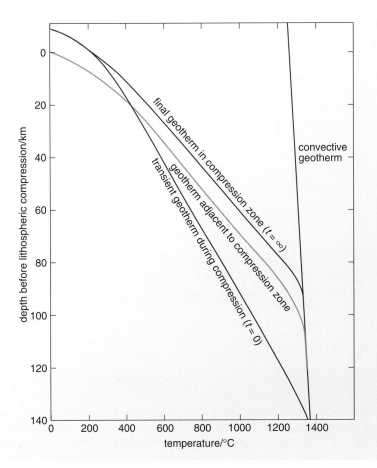

Figure 3.19 For the compression shown in Figure 3.18, the geothermal gradient initially flattens (the rate of change of temperature with depth decreases) and then steepens during thermal relaxation. As for Figure 3.16, it may help to turn the page around so that depth goes across the bottom of the Figure. Note that the data above the 0 km point on the vertical axis relates to uplifted crust following compression and thickening.

hardening will limit the progress of compression. For lower strain rates, if the relaxation process is able to keep up with the compression, the final geotherm (Figure 3.19) is parallel to the adjacent geotherm, but displaced slightly to the higher temperature side. Consequently, for low strain rates, the crust is thicker and hotter and so the lithosphere, due to strain softening, is able to continue to accommodate compression.

In this Section, you have seen how the crust–mantle boundary and the upper crust–lower crust boundary can change due to tectonic stresses. The crust–mantle boundary (the Moho) is determined seismically to be typically 30–50 km for continental lithosphere and 6–7 km for oceanic lithosphere. Of course, the thickness of the continental crust today is a consequence not only of the stresses in operation now, but of the accumulated effects of stresses that have long since been removed. Figure 3.20 shows how the Moho varies globally. To a first approximation, the Figure is consistent with what you already know about plate tectonics. The oceanic plates have a shallower Moho than the continents. However, there are places, such as Central America, where the Moho is more characteristic of oceanic lithosphere than continental lithosphere. The tectonic history of this region is complex and as you will see later in the second Video Band *Forging the land bridge* (Activity 4.1), the lithosphere is transitional. It is undergoing a process known as continentalization, whereby oceanic lithosphere, through prolonged volcanism and uplift, evolves towards continental lithosphere.

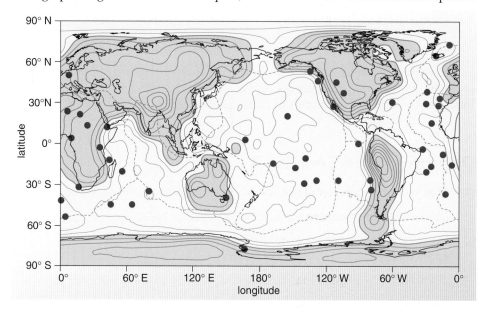

Figure 3.20 Global Moho depth variations. Contours are at 5 km intervals. The boundary between dark green (deeper) and light green (shallower) regions is 24 km. Red dots indicate location of hot spots.

Activity 3.1

You should now attempt Activity 3.1, which should take you about 1–2 hours and includes the viewing of the first Video Band. The exercise focuses on the evolution of the Basin and Range province and currently active extension in Death Valley, California. It will revise several concepts developed so far in this Course.

3.5   Summary of Section 3

In this Section, you have seen how the thickness of the crust and upper mantle and the lithosphere as a whole can vary with the temperature profile. The strength of the lithosphere depends on its thickness and temperature. The behaviour of the lithosphere when subjected to stress depends on the type of stress (extensional or compressional) and on the strain rate. Stresses acting on the lithosphere are not necessarily constant and they are not necessarily simple, in that they comprise components acting in different directions at different rates. It is the sum of these stresses and how they oppose one another within the lithosphere that are important. The main points are summarized in Table 3.3.

Table 3.3 Summary of lithospheric stresses and their effects.

Extension	Compression
Oceanic lithosphere is stronger than continental lithosphere	Oceanic lithosphere is stronger than continental lithosphere
Deformation of oceanic lithosphere is unlikely unless stress is extreme (e.g. across ridges and above plumes)	Deformation of oceanic lithosphere is unlikely
Archean lithosphere is weaker than modern lithosphere	Archean lithosphere is weaker than modern lithosphere
At high strain rates ($>10^{-14}\,s^{-1}$), strain softening allows extension to continue across continental lithosphere and may eventually result in the opening of a basin or even an ocean	At high strain rates ($>10^{-14}\,s^{-1}$), strain hardening resists compression across continental lithosphere; the process can only continue at the edges of lithospheric plates, not within the plate
At low strain rates ($<10^{-16}\,s^{-1}$), strain hardening (upwards migration of the crust–mantle boundary) limits extension to a β factor of about 1.5	At low strain rates ($<10^{-16}\,s^{-1}$), strain softening (downwards migration of the crust–mantle boundary) allows compression to continue

Armed with your understanding of the thermal and mechanical factors governing lithosphere strength, we will use the final Section of this Block to illustrate some specific examples of plate-tectonic processes.

Objectives for Section 3

Now that you have completed Section 3, you should be able to:

3.1 Understand the meaning of the terms printed in **bold.**

3.2 Describe how temperature and time affect the response of a material to an applied stress.

3.3 Discuss why the upper mantle and lower crust behave in a ductile manner.

3.4 Describe the processes leading to whole lithosphere failure during extension.

3.5 Describe the processes leading to whole lithosphere failure during compression.

3.6 Discuss the relative strengths of cold and hot oceanic and continental lithosphere.

3.7 Understand the significance of variations in the depth to the Moho in terms of the thermal history of the lithosphere.

Now try the following questions to test your understanding of Section 3.

Question 3.11 Explain what is meant by the terms strain rate, elastic deformation, brittle failure and strain hardening.

Question 3.12 Explain the significance of strain rate in relation to the strength of continental lithosphere.

Question 3.13 Use DP and Figure 3.20 to comment on the type of lithosphere that may be found beneath Australia, Costa Rica, New Zealand and Iceland.

4   Plate tectonics revisited

In the previous two Sections, you saw how the strength of the lithosphere depends on its thickness and temperature. Section 1 covered the basics of plate tectonics and we now return to this subject applying your knowledge of rheology and heat flow to examine a few examples in more detail. You will discover that plate tectonics is more complex than you may have thought, but much more fascinating.

4.1   The subducting slab

In Section 1.3, you looked at the various forces acting on the tectonic plates. There is a good correlation between plate speed and length of subducting plate edge. Plate speed tends to increase with the age of the subducting slab. The most important force acting on lithospheric plates is slab–pull, due to the 80 km or so of relief at the base of the plate between the highest part where new lithosphere is formed and the lowest part where it is consumed back into the mantle. This gravitational slide is relentless but not rapid, because despite the impression given in many cartoon pictures of subduction zones and even Hollywood films (such as *The Abyss*), the angle of subduction is not more than about 30° at shallow depths. The **subduction hinge** actually occurs beneath the overriding plate and it is a broad region of flexure between depths of about 20 and 100 km. Slab subducting angles range from about 10° at shallow depth to almost vertical at the greatest depth. A true-scale image (Figure 4.1) shows how low the subducting angle can be.

Information gleaned from data such as those shown in Figure 4.1 suggests that models of subducting plates rolling down over a fixed hinge and sliding through a 'slot' in the mantle are oversimplifications. The data — mainly seismic — indicate that the hinge (where the subducting plate bends) rolls back oceanward away from the overriding plate. Since the overriding plate and the subducting plate move towards each other, the hinge must therefore also move in an absolute frame of reference.

There is clear evidence for hinge rollback in the Pacific Ocean. Subduction of the Nazca Plate beneath the South American Plate continues while the Nazca Plate moves at 46–51 mm yr^{-1} east and the South American Plate moves south-westwards at 35 mm yr^{-1} (see DP). This process can only be sustained if the hinge where the downgoing slab bends actually migrates westward with time.

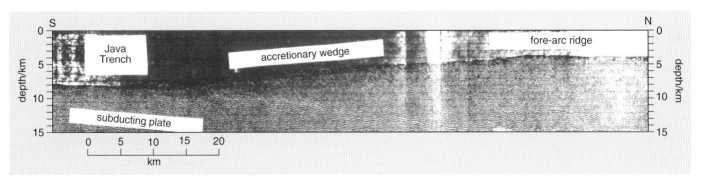

Figure 4.1   Seismic reflection profile across the Java Trench and associated accretionary wedge (or prism). Strong (bright) reflections highlight the top of the subducting slab.

The rate at which rollback occurs will vary with time. This is because plates do not collide head-on along the whole length of a plate: they all have some degree of rotation because they are moving over a curved surface and interacting with several other plates directly or indirectly.

4.1.1 The angle of subduction

The angle of subduction varies with time as you will see in the Video Band *Forging the land bridge* during Activity 4.1. The angle of subduction also varies with depth along the slab (getting steeper with depth) and it varies along the plate boundary.

- Why might subduction angles vary with distance along a plate boundary?

- The subduction process is driven by gravitational forces so variations in the relative densities of the downgoing and overriding slabs, caused by variations in the thermal and/or mechanical properties of the plates and the underlying asthenosphere, will result in differential forces being applied across the boundary.

The angle at which the subducting plate dips is given more accurately by seismic reflection data (as in Figure 4.1) than by the hypocentres of earthquakes defining the Wadati–Benioff zones.

- Why is this so?

- Wadati–Benioff zones define the instantaneous location of the slab surface. They show where the surface is at the time of the earthquake (whose source is at this surface): they do not show where the slab is going.

4.1.2 Tomographic imaging beneath north-eastern Japan

A wealth of information can be found in seismic data and advances in computer power and imaging facilities are continually being used to update and improve models. New methods pioneered by Dapeng Zhao and colleagues at the Tohoku University, Japan and the California Institute of Technology, USA involving not only the first arrivals of P- and S-waves, but also later arrivals, have been used to produce detailed 3D models of the subduction zone beneath north-eastern Japan to a depth of 200 km. Some 470 shallow and intermediate-depth earthquakes produced 18 679 arrival times at an array of almost 70 seismic stations (Figure 4.2).

Since the seismic stations and the earthquakes they detect are well distributed across the studied area, 3D images of the seismic structure may be derived. The easiest way to visualize the structure on the printed page is as 2D sections, so four sections A, B, C and D (Figure 4.3) are shown (Figures 4.4 and 4.5).

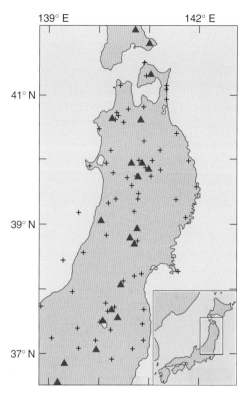

Figure 4.2 Seismic stations (crosses) used for the tomographic modelling described in the text. Triangles represent locations of active volcanoes. Inset shows extent of area studied in northern part of Japan.

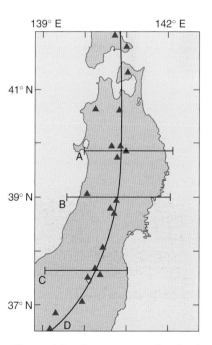

Figure 4.3 Location map for the three east–west profiles A, B, C along which seismic structures are depicted in Figure 4.4, and for the north–south profile D used in Figure 4.5.

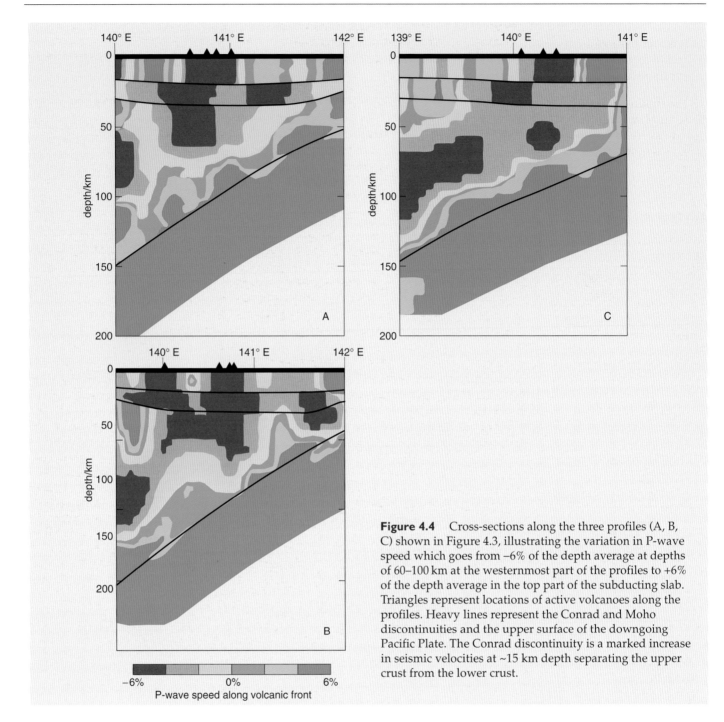

Figure 4.4 Cross-sections along the three profiles (A, B, C) shown in Figure 4.3, illustrating the variation in P-wave speed which goes from −6% of the depth average at depths of 60–100 km at the westernmost part of the profiles to +6% of the depth average in the top part of the subducting slab. Triangles represent locations of active volcanoes along the profiles. Heavy lines represent the Conrad and Moho discontinuities and the upper surface of the downgoing Pacific Plate. The Conrad discontinuity is a marked increase in seismic velocities at ~15 km depth separating the upper crust from the lower crust.

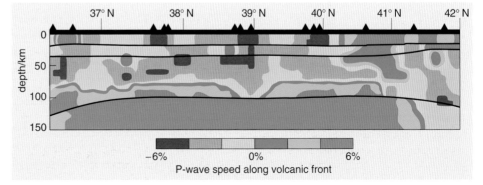

Figure 4.5 Cross-section along profile D (located on Figure 4.3).

Question 4.1 (a) Describe what you see in profile D (Figure 4.5). (b) If seismically relatively fast material represents cold, dense rock, while relatively slow material represents hotter, buoyant material, try to interpret your observations in (a).

As the subducting slab sinks and the overriding plate moves towards the rolling-back hinge, what happens to the mantle wedge in between the two? Seismic wave speed data (Figures 4.4 and 4.5) for the subducting slab beneath north-eastern Japan suggest that just above the subducting slab, in the lower part of the wedge, wave speeds are normal or slightly fast. Higher up in the wedge, there is an irregular zone about 50 km thick and 50 km above the slab surface characterized by relatively low speeds. At shallow depths, less than 75 km, the low-speed region steepens and defines hot, buoyant material beneath the active volcanoes.

In Section 2, you saw how increased temperature could weaken material. The low-speed region within the wedge described above is likely therefore to be weaker than the rest of the wedge. It is literally pulled apart by the relative movements of the downgoing slab and the overriding plate. Thus, at shallow depths, the slab slides past the base of the wedge, while simultaneously the slab and wedge are coupled and sink together, away from and opening up the low-speed region (Figure 4.6). There may be rather less coupling and shearing at greater depth.

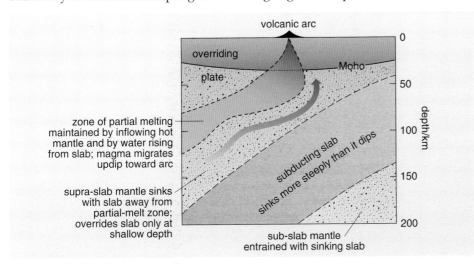

Figure 4.6 Cartoon illustrating the active process of subduction as deduced from seismic tomography. The subducting slab shears past the shallow updip part of the overlying mantle wedge. The lower part of the wedge sinks with the slab and pulls away from the inland and upper wedge across a zone of partial melting.

4.1.3 Implications for subduction

If a subducting slab sinks, displacing downwards mantle material, this must somehow be balanced above the slab to prevent a huge void forming or a massive depression in the surface above. The inclined low-speed region (Figure 4.4) may represent a compensating flow of rising hot mantle, which reaches its solidus as it becomes depressurized.

Arc volcanoes typically occur about 100 km above the tops of subducting slabs. Water released by dehydration of the slab is thought to produce partial melts within the overlying wedge, which in turn may feed the volcanic arc. However, there is a wide range of depths over which these dehydration processes can occur, so why should they always occur 100 km below volcanic arcs? Evidence from seismic tomography (Figures 4.4 and 4.5) suggests that there is not a simple vertical feeding mechanism from the downgoing slab at 100 km depth to the volcanoes at the surface. Thus, the lowest part of the wedge below the volcanoes cannot be the site of melting. Instead, the mantle melts which feed arc volcanoes may actually be generated where rising water from the downgoing slab intersects fertile (non-depleted), hot, obliquely rising mantle in the low-speed part of the wedge (Figure 4.4). Partial melts then migrate up the zone to enter the crust in a narrow band to feed the arc (Figure 4.6). The localized nature of the volcanic arc above a subducting slab may therefore owe at least as much to the flow of fresh mantle material into the wedge as to the exact location of slab dehydration.

Long-lived, steady-state arc magmatism is another feature not compatible with the 'injection down the slot' model of subduction. Although a sinking slab could release water continuously, the overlying mantle wedge would soon become cold and depleted. Only by the rise of new, hot mantle material into the low-speed region of the wedge can the supply of heat and volatiles be maintained.

4.2 Hot spots and mantle plumes

Hot spots are characterized by voluminous volcanism. They are mostly found near divergent plate boundaries and never near convergent boundaries. Hot spots are associated with long wavelength positive free-air anomalies, and are generally located above low seismic wave speed regions in the lower mantle and very low-speed patches at the core–mantle boundary. Local and regional tomographic images, such as those described in Section 1.5.1, can provide high-resolution images of plumes in the upper mantle, but the resolution at greater depth is poor and so little information can be obtained about the origin of plumes. The global tomographic approach, using earthquakes and seismic stations all over the world, provides lower-resolution images of plumes in the entire mantle. Dapeng Zhao's method for imaging mantle plumes takes into account the fact that the depth to the Moho and other seismic discontinuities is not the same everywhere. The Moho actually varies in depth from about 10 km under oceans to 40–70 km under continents. In addition, instead of using blocks in the model as described in Box 1.1, grid nodes are used which eliminate the huge vertical and lateral discontinuities in physical properties that characterize the block models even when the blocks are small. Grid models can image both small- and large-scale anomalies. Data collected

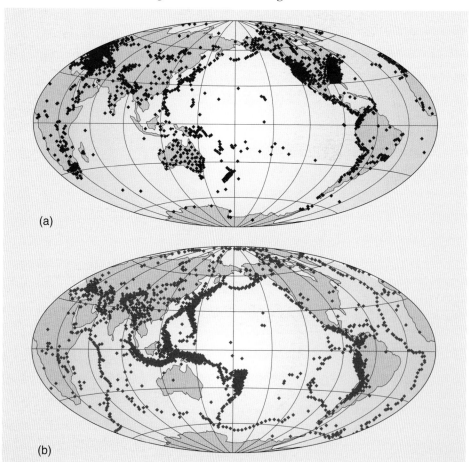

Figure 4.7   Data used to produce the tomographic images described in the text. (a) Locations of 5644 international seismological centre stations. (b) Epicentres of 7128 earthquakes that occurred between 1964 and 1998.

from a worldwide array of seismic stations between 1964 and 1998 have been reprocessed. Some 7128 events recorded at 5644 stations produced over 1 000 000 arrival times which were input to the models (Figure 4.7). Of course, earthquakes are not uniformly distributed around the globe and this technique does rely mainly on naturally occurring seismic events, but the distribution, though clustered along plate boundaries, is truly global.

This new method, which has much better resolution than previous tomographic methods, is able to resolve slow anomalies under hot-spot regions from the crust all the way down to the core–mantle boundary (Figure 4.8). Beneath both Hawaii and

Figure 4.8 Vertical cross-sections of P-wave speed images: under Hawaii (a) west–east and (b) south–north; and under Iceland (c) west–east and (d) south–north. Red and blue colours denote slow and fast speeds respectively. (e) Profile locations are shown. Red dots mark the locations of hot spots.

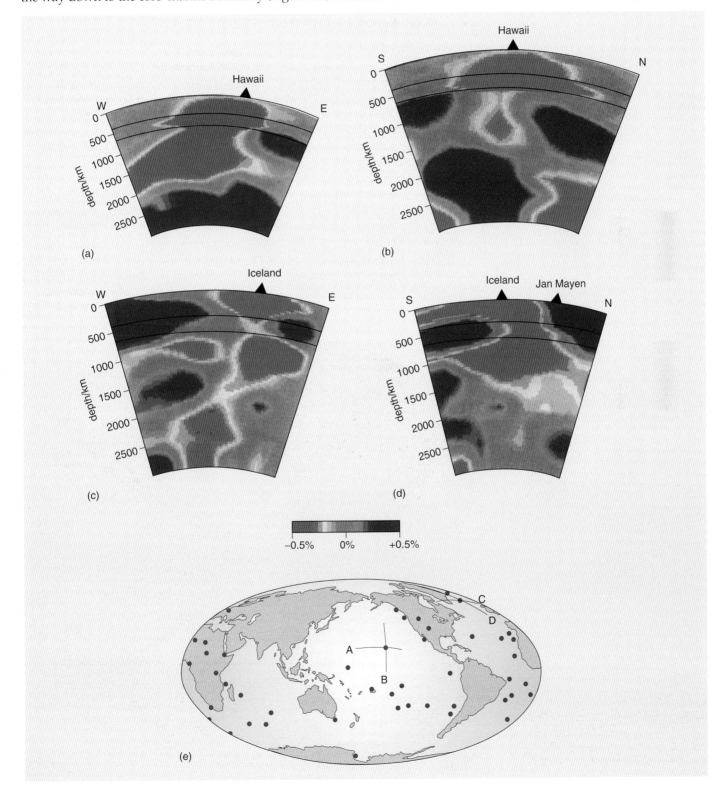

Iceland, using this method, anomalously slow speeds are observed all the way to the core–mantle boundary. The Hawaii plume is clearly much broader than the Iceland plume which explains why it is not detected at depth with the lower resolution methods. The effect of allowing for the natural variations in depth to the seismic discontinuities is to reduce some travel times by up to 9%.

A large low-speed region (red) runs from the surface to about 2000 km depth just west of Hawaii (Figure 4.8). A fast anomaly (blue) runs from about 1500 km depth to the core–mantle boundary south of Hawaii. Between about 670 km and 1500 km, a low-speed region seems to connect with the 2000-km-deep low-speed zone. This could be the mantle plume feeding the Hawaiian hot spot.

A low-speed region is also apparent beneath Iceland using this high resolution method (Figure 4.8).

● Describe the Iceland plume as imaged in Figure 4.8.

● The Iceland plume appears to be narrow in the east–west direction but wider in the north–south direction. The low-speed region extends south at depths less than 400 km.

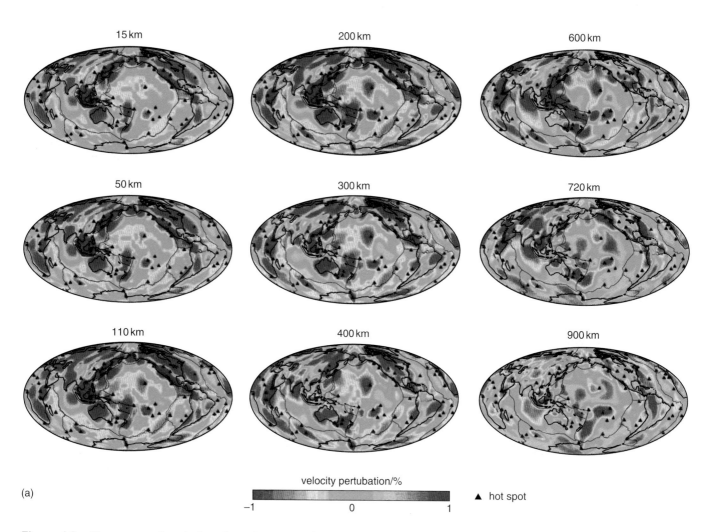

(a)

Figure 4.9   P-wave speed variations from the expected speed for various depth slices of mantle. Reds denote relatively slow regions and blues are relatively fast. Triangles denote hot-spot locations.

In answer to Question 1.6, you concluded that there was no anomalous wave speed deeper than 670 km beneath Iceland. The new global tomography seems to indicate that the Icelandic plume does actually extend down to the core–mantle boundary.

Mantle plumes are deflected by flow within the mantle, so they are not necessarily vertical pipes, and may even move with time. Plumes begin with a thermal and/or mechanical instability at depth. When hot material in the source layer is tapped by a hot spot faster than it can be regenerated by thermal conduction from below and recharged by the influx of new material from the sides, the plume will decline. A plume will continue to grow if the source layer thickens faster than the plume is tapped.

If plumes can be deflected by mantle flow, it follows that hot spots are not fixed though their velocities relative to the lithospheric plates are very small.

Most surface hot spots are located above low-speed anomalies in the lower mantle that extend down to the core–mantle boundary (Figure 4.9a).

However, some hot spots do not seem to be related to an underlying low-speed region in the lower mantle or core–mantle boundary. This may be because even this method is not producing sufficiently high-resolution images. It may be

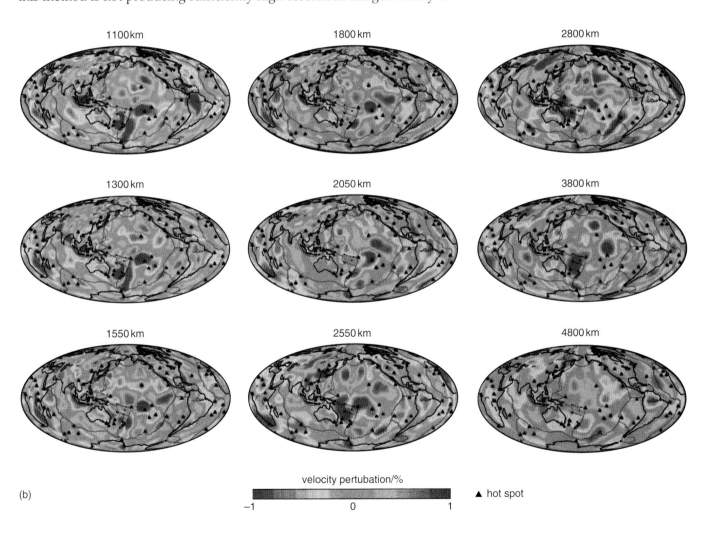

(b)

velocity pertubation/%

−1   0   1

▲ hot spot

because the plumes have been displaced laterally by mantle flow or it may even be because they simply do not extend to that depth. Strong plumes such as the Hawaii plume obviously extend to the core–mantle boundary. Some weaker plumes, such as those feeding hot spots beneath the South American and African Plates, may originate in a source layer close to the transition zone due to small-scale convection at the edges of continental cratons (see Question 1.7).

4.2.1   Hot spots and magma production rates

The dimensions of a mantle plume are not a clear indicator as to the productivity of the overlying hot spot. The very low-speed anomaly in the South Pacific (Figure 4.9) actually feeds several hot spots. However the productivity of all these hot spots put together does not match that of the Hawaiian hot spot. The Hawaiian plume though is relatively small. The high productivity of the Icelandic plume may be explained by the relatively thin lithosphere — and therefore higher heat flow and a shallower solidus (Section 2.4) in the region.

However, the higher productivity of the Hawaiian hot spot on moderately thick lithosphere requires an explanation. The Hawaiian volcanoes erupt picritic magmas that could be the product of melting eclogite and peridotite. It may be that the amount of eclogite (recycled old oceanic crust) affects the productivity of a hot spot. Thus, the chemistry of the mantle and the physical properties of the source layer dictate the nature of the hot spot above a mantle plume.

4.3   Concluding remarks

As with so many aspects of science, the more you know, the more you know you don't know. We can imagine plumes and speculate how they feed hot spots, but the more closely you look into it, the more you see there are substantial differences between the plumes. Experiments using tanks that look a bit like very wide-bottomed lava lamps, and computer simulations, have been run to investigate the processes that start and then maintain mantle plumes. One theory is that a massive impact on one side of the Earth could produce shock waves that would disturb the core–mantle boundary and produce a plume on the opposite side of the Earth. Theories and speculation abound and this is a fascinating area of ongoing research. Plumes and hot spots interact with the lithosphere — as you will see in the following Activity and again later in the Course.

Activity 4.1

You should now attempt Activity 4.1 which will take you about one hour to complete. It uses examples in Costa Rica to illustrate the plate-tectonic concepts already covered and considers some broader issues resulting from plate tectonics.

4.4 Summary of Section 4

- Subducting plates do not simply fall down a 'slot' into the mantle.

- The subduction hinge rolls back oceanward away from the overriding plate.

- The subducting slab sinks more steeply than it dips.

- The mantle wedge above a subducting slab must be replenished with fresh mantle material in order to feed arc magmatism.

- Global tomography using nodes rather than blocks has much higher resolution than other tomographic methods.

- Using this method, a low-speed region can be resolved running from the core–mantle boundary to the Iceland hot spot.

- Mantle plumes may be deflected by mantle flow and so may the overlying hot spot, but at a very low rate compared with plate-tectonic speeds.

- Big plumes do not necessarily underlie highly productive hot spots.

- Hot-spot productivity depends on the plume feeder and the amount of entrained eclogite.

- Costa Rica is located on continental lithosphere which has evolved through plate tectonic processes from an immature island arc to its present setting.

Objectives for Section 4

Now that you have completed Section 4, you should be able to:

4.1   Understand the meaning of the terms printed in **bold**.

4.2   Describe the subduction process in terms of absolute plate movements and the forces involved.

4.3   Make basic interpretations of global tomographic images and be aware of their limitations.

4.4   Understand the relationship between mantle plumes and hot spots.

4.5   Summarize in general terms the geological history of Costa Rica.

Now try the following questions to test your understanding of Section 4.

Question 4.2 Explain why hot spots are not necessarily 'fixed'.

Question 4.3 Describe the process of terrane accretion as it relates to Costa Rica. Is it an essential feature in the continentalization of the lithosphere?

Answers and comments to Questions

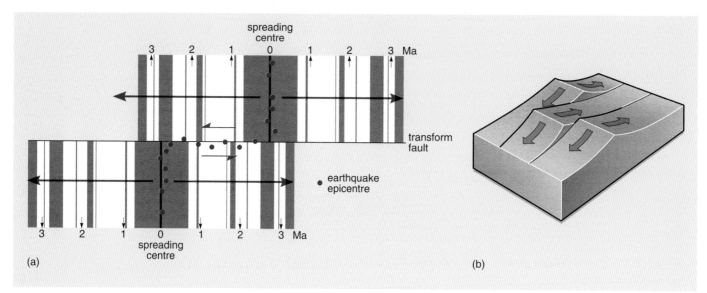

Figure A1.1 Sketch of relationships and sense of motion of transform faults. (a) A transform fault displaces a mid-ocean spreading centre and the magnetic stripes produced by it at different times. Opposed motions of the lithosphere occur only between the offsets of the spreading centre, which is where the transform fault is seismically active. Its sense of motion is opposite to that of displacements of the ridge and magnetic anomalies. Beyond the zone of active strike–slip motion the transform is inactive, and forms a fracture zone in the oceanic lithosphere. (b) The elevation of the ocean floor descends away from active spreading centres, so that transform faults and fracture zones have associated escarpments. In some cases magma 'leaks' to the surface along these zones.

Question 1.1 Figure A1.1 shows that seismicity associated with the transform fault occurs only along that part between the offset ridge axes. The sense of offset of the ridge axis is the opposite to that revealed by magnetic ages either side of a point on the transform fault. Taking into account the spreading of oceanic lithosphere away from the offset ridge segments explains both features. Between the ridge segments the spreading directions are opposite, so there is relative motion along that part of the transform. Beyond the zone of offset, present spreading is in the same direction and at the same rate either side of the fracture zone. Consequently, in that position there is no slip on one side relative to the other, and the fracture is seismically quiet. The displacement of magnetic stripes across it shows that it was once active when that part of the ocean floor was between offset ridge segments.

Question 1.2 (a) The islands and seamounts of the chain are much younger than the ocean floor on which they sit. The Hawaiian Islands are over 6000 km from the nearest spreading ridge and assuming a spreading rate of about 100 mm yr^{-1} this makes the age of the oceanic lithosphere in that vicinity about 60 Ma. (b) The best-fit line through the age vs. distance plots gives a length of 3500 km for the chain after about 40 Ma. So the average speed is $3500 \times 10^6/40 \times 10^6$ mm yr^{-1}, which comes to about 87 mm yr^{-1}. (c) For the older part of the chain, the gradient is slightly steeper, moving up to about 5900 km at 80 Ma. Thus the average speed for the period 40–80 Ma is $(5900-3500) \times 10^6/(80-40) \times 10^6$ mm yr^{-1} which comes out to about 60 mm yr^{-1}.

You may also have noticed (on Figure 1.6 and DP) that about 40 Ma ago the direction of motion of the Pacific Plate changed, which accounts for the Hawaii–Emperor Bend. Whatever occurred at that time, it involved a change in both plate speed and direction.

Question 1.3 Magmatic processes at the ridge emplace magma as extension proceeds. Magma reaching the surface wells out to form submarine lavas, with characteristic pillows because of the rapid chilling of the outer parts of each extrusion. At deeper levels, the conduits for magma solidify as vertical sheets, or dykes, of basalt to form a sheeted-dyke complex. Ponding of magma deeper still forms magma chambers in which fractional crystallization results in layered gabbros and ultramafic cumulates. These three layers, together with sediments that slowly accumulate on top of the ageing igneous rocks, constitute the oceanic crust. Beneath them reside mantle rocks that are the residues of partial melting to give the fourth, depleted peridotite layer.

Question 1.4 The main forces operating are shown on Figure A1.2. (a) Slab–pull and subduction–suction are the main forces that put the back-arc under tension. Ridge–slide is a consequence of the initiation of back-arc spreading. (b) Possible sources of magma are in the ascending asthenosphere beneath the spreading axis, or, conceivably, from the deep part of the subduction zone below the axis. (c) Because new lithosphere forms as a result of the spreading, in exactly the same way as at an oceanic spreading axis, albeit much more slowly, the axis must move towards the left of the diagram.

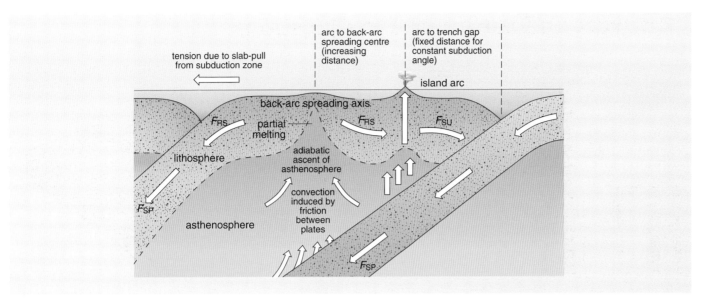

Figure AI.2 Annotated version of Figure 1.13. Exaggerated section across the Mariana and Ryuku arcs.

Question 1.5 (a) 40 mm yr^{-1} for 150 Ma gives a total length of 6000 km — implying a huge area of ocean, almost twice the width of the present Atlantic. Since the ocean ridge has now reached southern California, the whole of this length must have been subducted — except for some low-density fragments! (b) Any continental fragments separated during initial extension of the continental lithosphere must lie on the opposite side of the new ocean ridge from the main continental mass (in this case, the Eurasian and Australasian block). Any such separated fragments would remain on the eastern side of the Pacific ridge and become swept up by the Americas, as they moved west. (As you may realize, the situation is even more complicated because the modern Pacific grew from the eastern end of Tethys: North America and Asia have never been joined along their present Pacific coastlines). (c) Given the large area of ocean available for subduction (a), and the possibility that continental fragments could be carried on the eastern Pacific Plate, the Coney, Jones and Monger model seems satisfactory. They argue that old ocean lithosphere must have been present in the eastern Pacific presumably before North America overrode this part of the ocean, in which case the lithosphere may have become sufficiently dense to fail, subduct and form island arcs, which would also become accreted.

Question 1.6 (a) Beneath Iceland are 'warm' colours, signifying low S-wave speed and hot mantle. These extend to the 670 km discontinuity, and at deeper levels there is neither any clear structure in the tomograph nor much sign of any deviation in speed from what is expected — the colours are dominantly yellows. (b) Although Iceland is underlain by anomalously hot mantle, it is not resolved deeper than the 670 km discontinuity; there is no sign of any plume-like feature in the lower mantle. (c) Greenland, north-eastern North America, and Europe are underlain by upper mantle with anomalously high wave speeds, down to about 300 km, showing that the mantle is cool beneath

these segments of the continents. However, the south-western USA (Basin and Range Province) and north-east Africa and the Middle East are underlain by shallow, anomalously warm mantle. The blue, cold patches in the lower mantle beneath North America and Europe are large enough for them to represent true patches of high rigidity mantle, but their origins are obscure.

Question 1.7 South Africa is underlain mainly by low velocity material in the east and higher velocity material to the west to about 600 km. There is no image here of the 670 km discontinuity, but at 1300 km slower material in the southern and south-eastern region dominates. A more detailed series of images of the velocity structure is given in Figure 4.9, where it can be seen that the slow material feeding the last African hotspot disappears below 720 km. As you saw in Figure 1.19, southern Africa seems to be the source of a mass of low-speed mantle that is rising obliquely to the region of the Red Sea. However, Figure 1.20 indicates that there is a great deal of the deepest mantle that potentially could do the same. Does this presage mighty events in the future? Clearly it is both hard to tell and premature to worry!

Question 1.8 Geoscientists can locate and date magnetic reversal stripes over the Earth's recent past. Volcanic islands that have developed over hot spots, like Hawaii, can be dated and show that oceanic plates move relative to the global constellation of hot spots. Earthquakes are in fact generated by movements between blocks of the Earth's crust, and they are commonly found along plate boundaries, suggesting constant plate movement. Geological features which once were continuous, like the cratonic areas and mobile belts of South America and Africa, are now separated by oceanic material. This suggests that the continents have moved apart for the time-span indicated by the age of the oceanic lithosphere.

Question 1.9 Basalts are erupted onto the ocean floor at oceanic spreading centres. Mafic lavas contain relatively high amounts of the magnetic iron oxide magnetite, which acquires a magnetization in the same direction as the Earth's magnetic field. Since the Earth's magnetic polarity switches periodically from north to south (normal and reversed), ocean-floor basalts acquire a striped pattern of positive and negative magnetic anomalies, which relates to their age. Geoscientists study these stripes to erect a magnetic time-scale, i.e. a chart of magnetic reversals over the Earth's past, back to the early Jurassic Period. Comparing the record of stripes in any particular part of ocean floor with the standard magnetic time-scale gives the age range of that part of ocean floor. Dividing the width of the segment of ocean floor by the time range gives the half-spreading rate at the relevant ocean ridge. Magnetic stripes also provide a means for dating ocean basalts, for paleolatitude calculations and for charting past plate movements and interactions.

Question 1.10 Evidence from volcanic island chains, such as the Hawaii-Emperor chain in the Pacific, suggests that plates move over hot spots. Such chains have active volcanoes over a hot spot in the deeper mantle. The more distant in the chain from the active centre that now-inactive volcanic islands or seamounts are, the greater is their age. These features suggest that the lithospheric plate, on which an island chain sits, moves relative to the hot spot, whose source can be inferred to lie beneath the lithosphere. Comparing volcanic island chains (hot-spot trails) on one plate with those on adjacent plates indicates that all known hot spots are fixed relative to each other, but not necessarily to the absolute reference point, which is the Earth's centre. The hot-spot reference frame therefore provides the best possible evidence for the true or absolute movement of plates over time.

Question 1.11 Earthquakes occur at every type of plate boundary, so their locations do not by themselves distinguish between plate boundary types. The critical information is their depth, strength and sense of movement revealed by analysis of seismological records at stations distributed around the world. Shallow-focus earthquakes (<60 km deep) are associated with constructive and conservative margins, and with the oceanward side of a Wadati–Benioff zone. Deep-focus earthquakes (>60 km deep) are almost exclusively associated with destructive plate margins, either island arcs or ocean–continent destructive margins. Strong earthquakes typically occur at destructive margins, while within-plate areas are characteristically quiet, seismically. Therefore, distributed zones of shallow and deep earthquakes, some of them strong, characterize destructive plate margins, while exclusively shallow linear earthquake zones characterize both conservative (transform faults) and constructive plate margins. Some of the largest earthquakes occur along major conservative margins, such as the San Andreas Fault, but they have shallow foci. Studies of the first motions of seismic waves that arrive at the world-wide network of seismographic stations provide information that 'fingerprints' the sense of movement involved in an earthquake. Constructive-margin earthquakes have dominantly extensional senses of movement. Those at conservative margins are mainly strike–slip. Earthquakes at destructive margins always have a compressional component, but may involve strike–slip motions, depending on the directions of opposed movement of the two plates — many involve oblique senses of approach.

Question 1.12 See Table A1.

Table A1 Answer to Question 1.12.

Geoscientific feature	Destructive margin	Constructive margin	Conservative margin
Shallow-focus earthquakes (<60 km)	√	√	√
Deep-focus earthquakes (>60 km)	√		
Active volcanoes	√	√	
Wadati–Benioff zones	√		
Transform faults			√
Offset magnetic stripes			√
Magma generation	√	√	
Accretionary prisms	√		
Fracture zones			√
Island arcs	√		

Question 1.13 (a) Slab–pull is caused by gravity. The cold, dense subducted plate sinks under its own weight into a hotter mantle, until it is completely dewatered and of a comparable density and temperature to its surroundings. Slab–pull is dependent on slab descent angle, and the slab–pull force is greater for steeply dipping subduction zones. (b) Slab–pull cannot be the only plate-driving force, because at least one moving plate, the African Plate, has no attached subducting oceanic plate. Whilst the rate of movement of the African Plate is slow, it is actually moving. Similarly, the South American Plate is moving and has no attached subducting slab, although it is linked to a subduction zone on its west side.

Question 2.1 (a) The values of the temperature difference between the hot and cold regions and the thermal conductivity of the material. (b) The density difference between the hot and cold regions which is also temperature-dependent. (c) The opacity to radiation of the medium through which the heat is transferred is critical here. (d) The ease with which vertical movement can take place is important and this will depend on the rigidities of both the surrounding and advecting material.

Question 2.2 Convection occurs when hotter, more buoyant (due to lower density) material is overlain by cooler, heavier material. There must also be lateral density variations in the material (in addition to the vertical variations just described) so that the underlying material can form upwelling columns. In the solid mantle, the analogy of the wooden shelf applies. For a stress applied over a short time frame — such as a karate chop — the shelf responds in a brittle fashion. Over long periods, under the weight of several OU courses, the shelf bows and deforms like a very viscous fluid. The Rayleigh number for the mantle (the product of several variables including viscosity) is high, suggesting that not only does the mantle convect but it does so turbulently. The movement of course is slow and is accommodated by crystal creep.

Question 2.3 (a) For conductive heat flow, the geotherm will be straight and of the general form of the upper parts of the curves in Figure 2.1. The gradient (steepness) of the geotherm will depend on the parameters chosen for the model. (b) Below the oceanic lithosphere is the asthenosphere, which transports heat by convection. The process of convection brings hot material upwards and cold material downwards so that for the vertical range over which convection occurs, temperature increases with depth much more slowly than in the conductive region.

Question 2.4 Following the style of the oceanic heat flow description, continental heat flow can be summarized thus. Heat flow decreases rapidly (or exponentially) from values in excess of $120 \, \text{mW m}^{-2}$ for very young continental lithosphere to about $50 \, \text{mW m}^{-2}$ by 1000 Ma (Figure 2.9). After that age, heat flow remains constant at around $50 \, \text{mW m}^{-2}$ even for the very oldest provinces on Earth.

Question 2.5 The boundary layer model allows for the thickness of the lithosphere to increase with age. The decrease in heat flow with increasing age is then due to the increased thickness and the basal temperature remains constant. In the plate model, the lithosphere behaves as a cooling boundary layer of constant thickness. For young oceanic lithosphere (<70 Ma), both models fit the data well. The boundary layer model is consistent with seismic data for young lithosphere which suggest thickening lithosphere away from the ridge axis. The plate model is consistent with the heat flow data for lithosphere older than about 70 Ma (Section 2.4 and Table 2.3).

Question 2.6 Using Figure 2.6, the depth of the boundary is determined by extrapolating downwards the conductive (upper) part of the geotherm until it intersects the upwards-projected convective part of the geotherm. The base of the lithosphere is therefore within the thermal boundary layer and below the rigid mechanical boundary layer.

Question 2.7 Heat is generated at shallow depths within continental lithosphere and so for a given surface heat flow, the temperature at depth must be lower in continental than in oceanic lithosphere. Otherwise, continental heat flow would be much greater than oceanic heat flow. Continental lithosphere is thicker because of this lower temperature. [You should recall the question in Section 2.3 on lithosphere thickness on a much hotter Earth. Higher temperatures (and shallower melting) imply thinner lithosphere.]

Question 3.1 $10^{-15} (\text{s}^{-1}) = \dfrac{\text{change in length (m)}}{1 \, (\text{m}) \times 3.15 \times 10^{14} (\text{s})}$

Rearranging this becomes:

change in length (m) = $10^{-15} (\text{s}^{-1}) \times 1 \, (\text{m}) \times 3.15 \times 10^{14} (\text{s})$.

Thus, the change in a 1 m length of material over 10 Ma with a strain rate of $10^{-15} \, \text{s}^{-1}$ is 0.315 m, or just over 30 cm. This represents a 35% increase in length — but it does occur over a very long time-scale.

Question 3.2 Substituting into Equation 3.3 for a subduction rate of $1 \, \text{cm yr}^{-1}$:

strain rate $= \dfrac{10^{-2} (\text{m})}{1000 \times 10^3 (\text{m}) \times 3.15 \times 10^7 (\text{s})} = 3.17 \times 10^{-16} \, \text{s}^{-1}$.

Similarly, for a subduction rate of $3 \, \text{cm yr}^{-1}$:

strain rate $(\text{s}^{-1}) = \dfrac{3 \times 10^{-2} (\text{m})}{1000 \times 10^3 (\text{m}) \times 3.15 \times 10^7 (\text{s})} = 9 \times 10^{-16} \, \text{s}^{-1}$.

Thus, typical plate tectonic strain rates are of the order of $10^{-16} \, \text{s}^{-1}$.

Question 3.3 The geologically significant strain rate (deduced in the answer to Question 3.2) is $10^{-16} \, \text{s}^{-1}$. Drawing a horizontal line on Figure 3.8 at this value for strain rate, the temperature at which each of the curves intersects this line can be seen by joining the intersections to the temperature axis by five vertical lines. Thus, the strain rate of $10^{-16} \, \text{s}^{-1}$ for wet quartz is attained at 250 °C. For dry quartz, it is attained at 280 °C. For anorthite (Ca-feldspar) it is attained at 450 °C, for diopside (Ca–Mg pyroxene) it is attained at 500 °C and for olivine it is attained at 750 °C.

Question 3.4 Quartz and feldspar dominate the upper continental crust, while the upper mantle is dominated by olivine. From Figure 3.8, these became ductile for a strain rate of $10^{-16} \, \text{s}^{-1}$ at 250–280 °C, 450 °C and 750 °C respectively. Assuming the geotherm in Figure 2.12 applies, the temperature at which feldspar becomes ductile occurs at approximately 35 km depth, too deep to be considered as part of the upper crust. Quartz might start to become ductile, as much lower temperatures are required and these are achieved at <20 km, towards the base of the upper continental crust. The upper crust may therefore become strained, but it will not undergo ductile deformation as a whole. On the other hand, olivine needs to be hotter than 750 °C to be ductile, and this temperature is reached at about 60 km on the geotherm shown in Figure 2.12. Some ductile flow may begin to occur in the upper crust, but the crust is most likely to behave elastically and then to undergo brittle failure. Thus, the upper mantle is ductile and the upper crust is brittle.

Question 3.5 The stress involved in deforming the lithosphere (rather than moving it in the process of plate tectonics) is related to the difference in stresses — differences in magnitude and/or direction. Your annotated Figure should be similar to Figure A3.1.

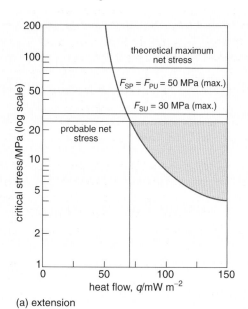

(a) extension

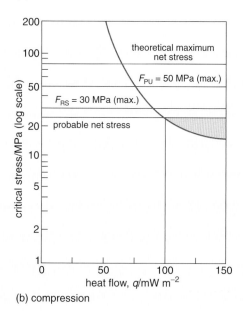

(b) compression

Figure A3.1 Annotated version of Figure 3.11 with the maximum values of stress shown. Symbols used are defined in Table 3.2.

Question 3.6 The theoretical maximum stress is the sum of the stresses acting in the same sense. It is not possible to be precise, as the stresses in Table 3.2 are ranges. The sum of the numbers given for extension applicable to continental lithosphere ($F_{SU} + F_{PU}$ = 30 MPa + 50 MPa = 80 MPa) is 80 MPa, but you should appreciate that the actual value is somewhat arbitrary. For compression, the theoretical maximum is 80 MPa ($F_{PU} + F_{RS}$). The heat flow required to achieve 80 MPa under extensional conditions is about 55 mW m^{-2}. To achieve 50 MPa under compression, heat flow in excess of 65 mW m^{-2} is required. In reality, the overall stresses are likely to be less than the maxima calculated here.

Question 3.7 Continental rifting will begin when the extensional stress is equal to or greater than the critical stress and whole lithosphere failure occurs. From Figure 3.11, it is clear that for a critical stress of 25 MPa, the minimum heat flow required for extension is about 70 mW. It can also be seen from the Figure that for much larger heat flow, the stress is much smaller. For example, for a heat flow of 100 mW m^{-2}, the critical stress is only about 8 MPa and easily attainable for the tectonic forces F_{SP} and F_{SU}.

Question 3.8 On Figure 3.11b, a horizontal line out from the stress axis at 25 MPa (half-way between the 20 and 30 MPa ticks) will intersect the curve at 100 mW m^{-2}. This is therefore the minimum heat flow required. The only places where heat flow of the order of 100 mW m^{-2} occurs are tectonically active and in an extensional regime. This means that major compressional deformation is not expected to occur within plates. Sufficiently high heat flow does not occur within plates away from an extensional regime.

Question 3.9 Initially, the geotherm intersects the convective geotherm at 1340 °C at 100 km depth. Thinning causes the geotherms to steepen and so, following the convective geotherm upwards, the base of the lithosphere rises to about 70 km depth. After thermal relaxation, the base of the lithosphere falls again to just below 100 km. The lithosphere has become stronger and slightly thicker.

Question 3.10 A β factor of 1.5 means that the ratio of initial to final thickness is 1.5 and therefore that the ratio of initial to final length (between two points across the stretched region) is 0.67. So, from Equation 3.3, for strain hardening, 10^{-15} s^{-1} = 0.5/t. Thus, $t = 5 \times 10^{14}$ s = 16 Ma. For strain softening, t = 1.6 Ma.

Question 3.11 Strain is the degree of deformation, which is the ratio of the change of length ΔL (or thickness) to the original length L (or thickness). Strain rate is literally the rate of change of strain and its units are s^{-1}.

Thus, strain rate = $\Delta L/Lt$ where t is the length of time over which the stress is applied.

Elastic deformation is the reversible deformation of a material caused by applying a stress. Brittle failure is the point at which a material breaks after a stress has been applied. It occurs after the elastic and plastic regions of the deformation/stress field have been exceeded. Strain hardening is the process by which, once it has previously been strained, a material becomes stronger and able to deform elastically under greater stresses.

Question 3.12 The time over which a stress is applied is highly significant and determines the way in which a material deforms. The everyday example of this is the wooden bookshelf that snaps under a short-duration high stress and bows under a prolonged stress. The geologically significant strain rate is $10^{-16}\,s^{-1}$ and strain rates less than this are termed slow. At low strain rates, extension is self-limiting due to strain hardening at a β factor of about 1.5. Strain hardening in this context involves thinning of the crust, replacing quartz and plagioclase by olivine to shallow depths where ductile behaviour is impossible for olivine. At high strain rates, extension can occur due to strain softening as the whole lithosphere thins, being replaced by asthenospheric material. This process may herald the beginning of continental rifting and eventually ocean spreading. For compression at low strain rates, strain softening permits compression to continue as the thickening crust puts more quartz and plagioclase to greater depths where the temperatures at which they begin to become ductile occur. In contrast, for compression at high strain rates, the whole lithosphere becomes thicker and therefore stronger and again the process is self-limiting.

Question 3.13 The Moho beneath Australia is >30 km deep (Figure 3.20) and therefore typical of continental lithosphere. This is an old, stable craton. Costa Rica is located on oceanic lithosphere undergoing the process of continentalization. The Moho is much shallower than is typical for continental lithosphere. New Zealand and Iceland appear to be similar. The Moho beneath New Zealand is about 17 km and beneath Iceland is <14 km (Figure 3.20). Both these locations are regions of active volcanism. Iceland is located astride the Mid-Atlantic Ridge and a mantle plume. New Zealand is part of a young island arc, and subduction occurs in a different direction in the North and South Islands. Thus, each of these locations, with the exception of Australia, is located on oceanic lithosphere that is developing and becoming more continental with time. Central America is much further advanced along this transition and Iceland will never get there.

Question 4.1 (a) Below about 100 km, the seismic wave speed is relatively high (+6%) although it decreases at the northern end of the profile. In the region 50–100 km, seismic speed is fairly normal although there are three 'pockets' of very low (−6%) speed. At shallow depths, less than 50 km, seismic wave speed is highly variable and is very low beneath most of the volcanoes. (b) Beneath most of the volcanoes there are regions of hot, buoyant material. The regions, which are small and localized, could be magma chambers. At depths of 50–100 km, broader regions of hot, buoyant material, which may feed the smaller regions above, extend down towards the relatively high-speed region at about 100 km. This high-speed region is the cold, subducting plate.

Question 4.2 It is not easy to find a stationary frame of reference on a spinning partly molten ball. It is therefore not surprising that while hot spots appear stationary over long time frames — certainly long compared with plate-tectonic processes (see Section 1.2, Figure 1.5), they may not really be stationary over longer periods. Tomographic images suggest that mantle plumes feeding hot spots are diverted by lateral mantle flow— possibly induced in part by the Earth's rotation — and so the overlying hot spots would be expected to migrate too in response.

Question 4.3 Strike–slip faults run approximately NW–SE in the southern part of Costa Rica. Dextral movements of hundreds of km have brought terranes from other tectonic settings and placed them on the edge of Costa Rica. Back-arc extensional regime dykes, pillow lavas, cherts and other rocks have been placed into a fore-arc position by this process. It is the evolving magmatic arc, though, and the formation of granites beneath the volcanoes that will eventually turn oceanic lithosphere into continental lithosphere.

Acknowledgements

Every effort has been made to trace all copyright owners, but if any has been inadvertently overlooked, we will be pleased to make the necessary arrangements at the earliest opportunity. Grateful acknowledgement is made to the following sources for permission to reproduce material within this Block:

Cover image Peter Francis/Open University; *Figure 1.1b* A. Smith (1996) *Plate Reconstructions* (CD-ROM), Cambridge Paleomap Services Ltd; *Figure 1.1d* A. Hallam (1975) 'Alfred Wegener and the hypothesis of continental drift', *Scientific American*, © Scientific American Inc., illustration by Lorelle Raboni; *Figure 1.3a,b* K. M. Creer (1965) 'Palaeomagnetic data from Gondwanic continents', in Blackett, P. M. S. *et al.* (eds) *A Symposium on Continental Drift*, The Royal Society; *Figure 1.3c* J. D. A. Piper (1987) *Palaeomagnetism and the Continental Crust*, copyright © 1987 Wiley; *Figure 1.4a* J. R. Hiertzler *et al.* (1966) 'Magnetic anomalies over the Reykjanes Ridge', *Deep Sea Research*, **13**, pp. 427–443, copyright © 1966 Elsevier; *Figures 1.4c, 1.5, 1.8* M. H. Bott (1982) *The Interior of the Earth: Its Structure, Constitution and Evolution*, Edward Arnold; *Figure 1.9* J. A. Grow (1973) 'Crustal and upper mantle structure of the central Aleutian arc', *Bulletin of the Geological Society of America*, **84**, Geological Society of America; *Figure 1.10* W. B. Hamilton (1988) 'Plate tectonics and island arcs', *Bulletin of the Geological Society of America*, **100**, pp.1503–1527, Geological Society of America; *Figure 1.11* D. B. Snyder and A. J. Barber (1997) 'Australian Banda Arc collision as the analogue ...', *Journal of the Geological Society of London*, **154**, The Geological Society; *Figure 1.12* R. G. Park (ed.) (1988) 'Divergent (extensional) tectonic regimes', in *Geological Structures and Moving Plates*, Kluwer; *Figure 1.15* P. J.Coney *et al.* (1980) 'Cordilleran suspect terranes', *Nature*, **188**, Macmillan; *Figure 1.16* artwork from *Scientific American*, June 1991, George V. Kelvin, © Scientific American Inc; *Figure 1.17* P. Kearey (1993) *The Encyclopedia of the Solid Earth Sciences*, copyright © 1993 Blackwell; *Figures 1.18, 1.19* J. Ritsema *et al.* (1999) 'Complex shear wave velocity structure imaged beneath Africa and Iceland', *Science*, **286**, copyright © 1999 American Association for the Advancement of Science; *Figure 1.20* Adapted from *Physics of the Earth and Planetary Interiors*, vol. 156, Lei, J. and Zhao, D. 'Global tomography: on the effect of various mantle and core phases', pp. 61–62. Copyright 2006, with permission of Elsevier; *Figure 1.21* R. D. Van der Hilst, S. Widiyantoro and E. R. Engdahl (1997) 'Evidence for deep mantle circulation from global tomography', *Nature*, **386**, Macmillan; *Figure 1.22* Prof. Louise H. Kellogg, Department of Geology, University of California; *Figures 2.1, 2.2* E. G. Nisbet and C. M. R. Fowler (1982) 'The thermal background metamorphism. I Simple one-dimensional conductive models', *Geoscience Canada*, **9**, pp. 161–164; *Figures 2.3, 2.8, 2.10, 2.12* C. A. Stein (1995) 'Heat flow of the Earth', *AGU reference shelf series*, **1**, American Geophysical Union; *Figure 2.4* C. M. R. Fowler (1990) *The Solid Earth: An Introduction to Global Geophysics*, copyright © 1990 Cambridge University Press; *Figure 2.7* B. Parsons and D. McKenzie (1978) 'Mantle convection and the thermal structure of the plates', *Journal of Geophysical Research*, **83** (B9) copyright © 1978 American Geophysical Union; *Figure 2.9* J. G. Slater *et al.* (1981) 'Oceans and continents: similarities and differences ...', *Journal of Geophysical Research*, **86**(B12) copyright © 1981 American Geophysical Union; *Figure 2.13* C. M. R. Fowler (1990) *The Solid Earth: An Introduction to Global Geophysics*, Cambridge University Press; *Figures 3.1a,b, 3.3, 3.4* T. B. Akrill *et al.* (1979) 'Material in tension', *Physics*, Edward Arnold Ltd; *Figures 3.5, 3.8–3.10, 3.13, 3.17* N. J. Kusznir and R. G. Park (1987) 'The extensional strength of the continental lithosphere', in M. P. Coward, J. F. Dewey and P. L. Hancock (eds) *Continental Extension Tectonics*, Geological Society Spec. Publ. No. 28; *Figure 3.6* G. Berrino *et al.* (1992) *Journal of Volcanology and Geothermal Research*, **53**, pp.11–26, Elsevier; *Figure 3.7a,b* Hazel Rymer/Open University; *Figure 3.11* R. G. Park (1988) 'The effect of extensional and compressional stress within plates', *Geological Structures and Moving Plates*, Kluwer; *Figure 3.12* Dave Rothery/Open University; *Figure 3.14* G. C. Brown and A. E. Mussett (1981) *The Inaccessible Earth*, Kluwer; *Figures 3.16, 3.19* J. F. Dewey (1982) 'Plate tectonics and the evolution of the British Isles', *Journal of the Geological Society of London*, **139**, Geological Society Publishing House; *Figure 3.20* T. Tanimoto (1995) 'Crustal structure of the Earth', in Ahrens, T. J. (ed.) *Global Earth Physics: A Handbook of Physical Constants*, *AGU reference shelf series*, **1**, American Geophysical Union; *Figures 4.1, 4.6* W. B. Hamilton (1995) 'Subduction systems and magmatism', in Smellie, J. L. (ed.) *Volcanism Associated with Extension at Consuming Plate Margins*, **81**, pp.3–28, originally in a *Geological Society Special Publication*; *Figures 4.2–4.5* D. Zhao *et al.* (1992) 'Tomographic imaging of P- and S-wave velocity ...', *Journal of Geophysical Research*, **97**(B13), copyright © 1992 American Geophysical Union; *Figures 4.7a,b, 4.8a–e, 4.9a,b* D. Zhao *et al.* (2001) 'Seismic structure and origin of hotspots and mantle plumes', *Earth and Planetary Science Letters*, **192**, pp.251–265, copyright © 2001 Elsevier.

Index

Note: bold page numbers denote where Glossary terms are introduced/defined.